THE
ENDLESS POSSIBILITIES OF
BEATRICE

DEDICATION

This book is dedicated to Princess Bundle, Copycat the Lionheart, Paddy, Duffy and Blot, who all took on the challenge of living with me at different times and taught me what it is to be Cat, in all its many forms.

Also to Mr Mao, Edna, Albert, DelBoy, Lilylou, Bumble, Booboo and Peanut (the original bionic cat) – and to all the cats of my life who have brought me joy and laughter and showed me the endless possibilities of being.

THE
ENDLESS POSSIBILITIES OF
BEATRICE

ANNIE GOODYEAR

But what if I should discover that I myself am the enemy who must be loved – what then?

Carl Jung

THE PROPHECY

When powers beneath meet powers on high
When time breaks open with a sigh
And breathes its pain into the air
Till fear and hate are everywhere,
Then one is born with many moods
Whose markings contain multitudes.
A power so great in one so small
Could be the saving of us all
But if those powers prove too fierce
What should be strength becomes a curse.

The Book of the Cat

On a hilltop overlooking the Far Dale and the Wildwoods a mighty stag stared down at a bundle of dirty cloth.

"Are we ready?" he asked his noble counsellors.

The badger and the owl and the fox nodded.

"It is time, my Lord," said the badger.

"We must take great care," said the fox.

"It is a risk," said the owl. "Once this is done, there is no undoing. No turning back. But it is a risk we have to take – for the Wildwoods and for all of us. The Prophecy must be fulfilled."

The stag paused for a moment, looking across his beloved Dale. Then he spoke again.

"Let it be done." He bent his head and gently lifted away the cloth with the tip of his antlers.

A great light shone. So bright they had to cover their eyes.

CHAPTER 1

THE MARKINGS OF SHAME

Her Royal Highness Princess Beatrice of the Wildwoods turned around slowly three times before settling down among the Christmas decorations. A strand of gold tinsel wound itself around her shoulders like a stole. It tickled a bit, but at least it was more comfortable than the red and green baubles she was lying upon. The trick, she had learnt, was to get the curves of the baubles tucked into the soft curvy places of her belly. But then if she needed to fidget a little, maybe to lick a speck of glitter off her side, or flick away some dust with her tail, they moved beneath her in a most unnerving manner.

Princess Beatrice's mother, the great Queen Sheba, scorned such cheap decorations. But then, as she liked to repeat at every opportunity, the Queen had been born in an Egyptian palace where the walls were covered with crystals and diamonds. Not an attic full of cardboard boxes like the one in which they now found themselves.

Beatrice liked the bauble box. It was not always comfortable but the colours reminded her of something. All those bright blues and reds and greens. They were like a place she had dreamt of once, or a story that she couldn't quite remember. A fairytale, set among big skies dotted with bright birds, above grassy hills where deer leapt and where the rocks grew so huge it could take you a day to climb them.

And then, of course, there was something else about the

decorations box. When Beatrice sat among such colours she could hide from the world and forget for a while her own secret shame.

* * *

"Beattie, Beattie!" The voice that came up the stairs was harsh and over familiar – at least that was Queen Sheba's opinion. It belonged to the Lady-in-Waiting. The Lady lived downstairs and was responsible for such day-to-day matters as food, cleaning and general maintenance. Sheba had been very clear about the dangers of responding to such a summons.

"A name, Beatrice, is a sacred thing. It contains the essence of the soul. Why, there are some poor creatures in these woods with no name at all. Those wretched beings will do anything to acquire a name. Why, they might even try to steal yours if you let them."

"But how…?" Beatrice began.

"Enough, Beatrice! I fear I have said too much already. You are too young to understand these matters. But beware. Simply remember that when you respond to an improper form of address you deny your very being.

"One may, of course, have several names which each serve a different purpose. But they are names of one's own choosing, for use in particular circumstances. Some names may stay secret forever. Those are the parts of you that no one can touch. Meanwhile I advise you to be very careful with all public forms of address."

* * *

Beatrice tried to be careful. She really did. Sometimes she ignored the calls altogether and turned her head away. Occasionally she even resorted to spitting, always aware that spitting in excess could be vulgar in a Princess. But there were times when Beatrice forgot herself and her mother's

2

instructions entirely and ended up rolling around on the floor and allowing the Lady to tickle her tummy.

Queen Sheba was horrified. But then she usually was horrified about one thing or another. Beatrice's markings for a start – "All over the place, darling." Then there were her table manners – "NEVER finish the whole plate. One is not a dog!" And then there was Beatrice's unfortunate habit of playing with lager bottle tops if she found them lying around.

"Play is inevitable for kittens in the early years, I suppose," Sheba sighed, "but if you must do it, kindly remember it is champagne corks or nothing. Lager tops are for peasants."

Truth to tell, Princess Beatrice rather liked breaking the rules. Being a Princess was so boring. There did not seem to be any privileges, just a long list of things not to do.

But today was not a day for breaking rules or playing. Today there were her markings to consider. They had been misbehaving all day. She could not possibly allow anyone to see her in this state, especially the Lady. Beatrice tried to sneak a peek under the mounds of tinsel and baubles beneath her, but all she could see were the Christmas fairy lights. She sat very still. Could she feel something moving? There was a definite sliding sensation in the region of her tail. But she dare not turn to check it in case she showed something she should not. Better to stay completely motionless and hope everything else did too.

From somewhere she heard her mother's voice, echoing, distant. "Manage your markings, my girl, and you will manage your life. Remember the ancient Prophecy. Only when you are mistress of your markings will you truly inherit. And if you fail…." Sheba's voice always trailed away at this point so Beatrice had no idea what would happen if she failed. But she knew that she did not want to find out. Come to think of it, she did not actually know what the Prophecy was either, so she could not be blamed for not remembering it. From the way Sheba talked, it just sounded like a long list of things Beatrice had done wrong. Or might do wrong one day if she could not control her markings. She snuggled deeper down into the decorations, hoping they would hide her completely. Two strings of silver lameta dangled from her forehead.

"Beattie, what on earth are you doing hiding in that box? Wait a moment. I have got to get a photo of this."

The Lady was laughing at her. A mere servant, daring to ridicule a Princess! Beatrice felt waves of anger override her shame, followed by another very unpleasant sensation and it wasn't just the plastic doves of peace digging into her sides. This was different altogether – as though her fur was sliding in different directions all at once. As if she was dissolving from the outside in. There was no question of leaving the cardboard box now. She might have to stay there forever.

* * *

The markings had been a problem from the start. Or maybe not such a problem if you were a person who liked change. It was all very well for Sheba to tell her to manage her markings. Sheba did not have any to speak of. Sheba's fur was soft and long and dense, like a Queen's should be. She was pure white all over except for the merest tips of her ears and tail and the top of her nose, which were black. And most importantly, her markings never moved.

Beatrice, on the other hand, had three colours to worry about. She was black and gold and white, which the Lady for some unaccountable reason referred to as tortoiseshell.

"Really darling, I don't know why you are so upset. A tortoise is a very rare and valuable creature," said Sheba. "Why if you lived, God forbid, in America, they would call you a calico, which would be much worse."

"Why, what's calico?" asked Beatrice, grumpily.

"It's a rather primitive printed cotton, though I can see

4

how that might suit you – particularly today." Sheba sighed. "I, of course, would be glorious pure silk."

In any case, being called a tortoise or a calico were the least of Beatrice's problems. The real issue was with the three colours that she did have which were in the habit of running riot. They just moved about of their own accord.

Today, for instance, she had begun the day with a white front and a white tummy. Her ears were golden while her back and sides were a patchwork of black and white. Her tail was striped black and gold and her eyes were amber and jet. This morning her markings had been almost perfectly symmetrical.

"Yes, quite tidy today," Sheba had purred approvingly.

But it could all change at any minute.

Sometimes she turned round to find her tail had gone white. Sometimes the black slipped down the inside of her front legs so they looked bandy. Once, after a particularly bad dream, she woke up with a black body, a gold head and four completely white legs. Even Queen Sheba had raised a smile that morning, but poor Beatrice was mortified.

"It's not fair. You don't understand what it's like. Never to know what you will look like from one day to the next. To look ridiculous one day and beautiful the next and not to be able to do anything about it. How can I ever go out? No one will even recognise me. If they don't know who I am how will they know I am to be their Queen?"

The more upset Beatrice became, the more her markings moved and slid. It was as though they were alive.

"It's no good Mummy, I'll never be able to manage them. I'll never be a Queen like you."

For once Sheba didn't turn her face away and when she spoke her voice was gentle.

"No my dear, you will never be a Queen like me, but maybe that's a good thing. I am not sure I did so well in the end." The Queen sighed and glanced at the bare windows which

5

overlooked the sad grey trees which made up the equally sad grey woods stretching as far as the eye could see.

"Your markings are a trial now. But one day they may be the making of you. There was never a kitten like you and there never will be again. If I seem harsh at times it is because yours is a unique destiny. It is indeed as the Prophecy foretold.

"But just make sure you learn to manage those markings. Or else I am very much afraid they will manage you."

CHAPTER 2
CATIQUETTE

"Do stop doing that dear, it's so unbecoming."

Queen Sheba had woken up from her afternoon nap. Beatrice dropped the lager bottle top she had in her mouth. Carefully, she side-swiped it to the corner of the room so she would know where it was for next time.

"Now dear, it's time for Catiquette. Assume the position please. Today we are going to practise the Queenly Attitudes."

Beatrice hated the daily Catiquette lessons, but she did as she was told. Catiquette was all about doing and saying The Right Thing. Or at least The Right Thing according to Sheba. The Right Thing for a Queen, of course, was very different from The Right Thing for a Common Street Cat.

Beatrice had been studying Queenly Attitudes for weeks now and so she sat proudly upright, with her chin tucked in, her front paws neatly together and her tail wound tightly around them. The tip of her tail twitched ever so slightly, just so that anyone watching would know she was still ready for action if required. In theory, of course, any cat could do the same. But the royal secret lay in taking yourself back inside yourself somehow, pretending that your eyes were just windows which you could look through or hide behind. When you got it right you felt very safe and protected, and very powerful too. You could look out through your own windows but no one else could see behind them to where you really dwelt within.

The Queen made Beatrice practise this position every day for at least three hours, but she still wasn't very good at it. There was always a noise or a bird flying over or a shadow that flitted across the floor and just had to be pounced on. Then the inner Beatrice leapt out of her hiding place deep inside and chased the shadow or climbed onto the bookcase to pull faces at the birds through the window or rolled over and practised holding the bottle top between her paws and kicking it with her back legs at the same time.

Then she knew she was in trouble. The Queen would freeze over, her white fur like ice, and her face and belly turned away.

"No, don't come near me, I don't want to speak to a vulgar, common kitten. Somewhere in this dreadful, dirty room, there used to be a Princess. But obviously she has left the building."

When her mother became the Ice Queen in this way little Beatrice felt her own insides grow cold and lonely. If she had brothers and sisters she could have played with them, but she was an only kitten.

"It's a blessing there's only one of you. That's more than enough. Any more of this behaviour and it will be the pet shop for you. And then what will happen to our inheritance? Our Queendom?" Sheba paused to flick a speck of dust from her ears. "You, young lady, are our only hope. Heaven knows, your markings are bad enough. But when you behave like that, I feel that all hope is gone."

With a strangled sob the Queen lay down on the shabby brown carpet, her paws covering her eyes as though she could not bear to look at her daughter.

"But Mummy," whimpered Beatrice, climbing over her mother's back and thrusting her tiny black nose into the Royal Face, "we don't have a Queendom. We don't even have a crown."

8

The great Queen Sheba said nothing, but let out a sigh as cold and wintry as the east wind and moved further away. Beatrice shivered. She looked around the attic room for comfort. In the far corner lay the lager bottle top, where she had left it. That might be just the thing. She spent a few minutes putting it on top on her head and parading around imagining it was a crown. It was too small of course and fell off – which made quite a good game in the end.

* * *

Afternoon Catiquette lessons usually involved Contemplating Beauty. This was not about looking at works of art, or even nature, but the Full and Generous Appreciation of the Self. Sheba was particularly insistent on this quality.

"Knowing and appreciating one's own beauty at all times, in all places, under all circumstances – this is the key to happiness and to Queenliness. As you regard yourself, so others will regard you. To be a Queen in your own eyes is to be a Queen indeed."

Sheba's pronouncements were always of a universal and unilateral nature. Sometimes Beatrice thought it would be nice to have a proper conversation, even a discussion. But there was no time for questions. Sheba was in full flow.

"For some of us, of course, self appreciation is easier than for others. In my own case, for example, people have remarked on my great beauty since the day I was born, when I was still blind and couldn't even see myself. Now, of course, I know what they were talking about." She cast her eyes appreciatively over her lustrous coat and her thick, powerful tail.

"For me it was a simple step to breathe in the admiration and repeat it inwardly. 'Beautiful me…beautiful me… beautiful…me.'"

Sheba's eyes began to glaze over with the glory of herself. For a moment the grubby attic filled with a vast silence – the way the moon fills the sky on a twinkling winter night. But it was not to last. With the discipline of Queenly Attitudes applied daily over the years, Sheba gathered her beauty back into herself and returned to the matter in hand.

"Other, less fortunate kittens," here she looked at Beatrice with a smile both sad and superior, "have to work much harder. In your case, my dear, I suggest working from the inside out. Search for your inner beauty and when you find that the outer beauty will follow."

Sheba's voice sounded uncharacteristically weak and uncertain. "At least, that's what the Regal Manuals say Of course I wouldn't know myself, never having had to face that particular challenge." Her eyes became misty again as awareness of her splendour washed over her in a great wave.

"Anyway my dear, I am rather afraid I am getting one of my headaches. I need to go and lie on a feather duvet for a while. So I will leave you to practise by yourself."

And with that she swept out of the room.

* * *

Alone in the attic, Beatrice contemplated the challenge of Contemplating Beauty. Outer beauty she understood only too well from her mother. But inner beauty? How could she feel beautiful inside when all she ever got told was what was wrong with her? On those rare days when her markings fell just right she did feel better inside. Sometimes people even said she was pretty. But then just when she began to believe in her dainty white face and her golden ears, just when her black patches became glossy and smooth-edged and symmetrical, she would hear someone laughing and discover that a black splodge had slipped halfway down her nose. Or her tail had become an alarming shade of tabby. And she would feel such shame that the merest possibility of beauty disappeared like a rainbow.

10

Beatrice closed her eyes because she thought it would be easier to feel beautiful if she could not see herself. She tried and tried to sense the bliss that Sheba had talked about and so clearly experienced. But it was no good. All she could feel was a squirming and wriggling. Were her insides moving too? This thought was so alarming that Beatrice found herself leaping and jumping around the room, despite her very best efforts to stay still. The more she tried not to move, the more she needed to run.

Out of the corner of her eye she could see other things moving too around her – in the cardboard boxes, on the bookshelves, behind the saggy bed. And whether she wished it or not, she found her legs giving chase.

She ran and she jumped. She climbed the shelves, she pounced on the cushions. She clawed the carpet. And still the shadows moved, just out of vision. And still the wriggling inside her continued. As though it would never be still.

Eventually, when the boxes were all overturned and the books were knocked from the shelves to the floor, her legs could carry her no more. They simply folded themselves beneath her without warning. Exhausted from running, dismayed by her own failure and despairing at her lack of beauty, Beatrice crawled into a corner and began to wash.

She washed hard and furiously, her rough tongue lashing at her markings over and over. She would show them who was boss. Beatrice was so angry and upset she didn't even look where she was licking or see what had happened around her. She was sick to death of herself and her markings. She just wanted them gone.

All of a sudden, the temperature in the room dropped and the air became very still, like it did before a thunderstorm. Beatrice paused in her licking and looked up. Sheba loomed over her, white tail erect and three times its normal size. Her fury filled the room, so that Beatrice's own fur prickled and stood on end with fear.

"What on earth has been going on here?" Sheba's voice cut through the air like a claw. "Are we become a laundry? Have we turned into kitchen maids?" Her tail lashed furiously from side to side.

It was only then that Beatrice noticed what had happened to the room. Hanging from the ceiling, draped over the wardrobe, poking out of cardboard boxes, were patches of fur.

There were black patches and white patches and gold patches. There were squares and triangles and circles and long thin stripes and weird raggedy bits. There were even some stripy ones that hung across the ceiling like bunting. And, though she was trembling with fear, a tiny part of Beatrice still thought those looked quite fun.

"This, young lady – though I can hardly call you young lady now – this represents a total loss of control. Centuries of breeding and for what? No discipline, no focus, no royalty, no beauty. I feel ashamed. Quite ashamed."

To Beatrice's surprise Sheba turned and addressed the markings directly.

"Now I expect you all to return to your rightful places immediately. And that means NOW."

The Queen's voice had an edge that could slice through marble. Beatrice flinched. The next moment a great wind filled the room and everything went wild. The markings whirled and zoomed around the tiny attic, swishing and whooshing as they went, till Beatrice's ears were full up with the sounds and she became quite dizzy. Then all of a sudden they settled on top of her like a flock of birds and took up their most flattering positions. Beatrice looked at herself in amazement.

"Don't move." Sheba's voice was glass. Cold and clear and likely to shatter into sharp splinters at any moment. "Not a muscle, not an ear, not a whisker. Now look. Look inside. Feel the beauty."

But little Beatrice was so frozen with fear that she couldn't feel a thing.

Indeed, between them the two cats were so consumed by fury and fear that neither of them noticed a patch of black fur that was still hanging from the attic window and waving around in a rather jaunty fashion.

CHAPTER 3

A DARK STRANGER

"Get out! Get out of my palace this moment! Mummy, help! Get out now, I said! This minute!"

Beatrice had awoken from her afternoon nap to find a large scruffy black cat sitting confidently in the middle of the attic. What's more, he was looking right at her, quite regardless of Catiquette, which decreed that he should lower his eyes in the presence of royalty.

"Don't you know who I am?" Beatrice's meows were turning into hysterical squeals. The stranger just blinked and stared at her with a stupid, lazy grin on his face.

"Well," she continued, trying her best to sound like Sheba, "I'll have you know, I'm a Princess and you're…you're – well, you're no one. No one at all."

"That so?" The black cat spoke in a rather strange, slow drawl. Not at all like Sheba's clipped vowels. "Guess if I'm no one then I'm not here are all. So don't mind me ma'am." He paused to give his ear a good, long scratch. Oh no, not fleas as well, thought Beatrice. "Though if I was here, you and me could have a fine old time with all these boxes."

He began to jump from one big box to another, over and over. It was as though his feet were on springs. One by one the boxes tipped over, spilling out on the grubby carpet. Not just Christmas decorations but clothes and papers and pencils and cables and tennis balls and even an old violin and a battered guitar. The more chaos he created the more wild he became, crouching and leaping and rolling over till Beatrice became dizzy watching him. This would not do. She drew her paws together in the best Queenly Attitude she could manage.

"I demand that you identify yourself and then withdraw immediately."

"Identify myself? Gee, that's a good one." The visitor rolled over onto his belly and eyed her with amusement. "You mean you don't recognise me?"

"I've never seen you before in my life. And don't be so silly as to suggest that we might even remotely move in the same circles."

"You sure 'bout that?" The black cat flicked his tail nonchalantly. "Why, I would have said we was very well acquainted."

"You just wait till my mother comes back. She'll see you off the premises, dead or alive."

"Not the famous Sheba? That old fraud? Still hawking those tales about palaces and pyramids, I suppose." The intruder laughed. "Wonderful dame but past her prime.

"Now you, on the other hand," he eyed her up and down in an impudent manner, "I'd say you was just coming into yours." He winked impertinently. "But see here, young lady, aren't you missing something?"

"Missing? I...I don't know what you mean." Something about the stranger's tone and his familiar gaze made Beatrice feel all of a sudden very unsure of herself.

"Seems to me ma'am, if you don't my saying, that some of your markings seem to have...well, gone walkabout. If I didn't know you – and of course you insist that I don't, so I may be wrong – I'd say maybe you weren't all there?" And with that he laughed so much he rolled over three times, waving his long legs in the air and displaying a soft and ample belly.

Such vulgarity, Beatrice could hardly believe it. Maybe it was because he was foreign. He must be, with that accent.

Sheba held forth often on this subject. "Egyptians of course are fine. At least the ones who know their history. They know how to worship cats. But the rest! Common, lazy creatures for the most part. That's foreigners for you. No breeding, no manners at all."

Foreign or not, the stranger's comments on her markings caused Beatrice's belly to flip with fear. Well, some of her belly. Because as she looked down she saw to her consternation that the black markings on one side were gone. Not just moved, but gone altogether. And they appeared to have taken with them a section of her plump kitten's tummy, leaving her quite skinny. More worryingly, she had not even noticed them leave.

"Hey dude, don't worry about it. Here today, gone tomorrow. Or maybe it should be gone today, here tomorrow. Heh heh heh!" The black cat laughed uproariously at his own joke.

"Anyway, ma'am, allow me to introduce myself. Jake's the name, play's the game. At your service. Whatever game you have in mind, ma'am."

"Don't call me dude. And don't call me ma'am either." Beatrice knew she should find her visitor offensive but secretly she found his cheekiness was rather attractive. The attic could be very boring and lonely at times. Nevertheless there were some boundaries.

"Most people refer to me as Your Royal Highness, the Princess Beatrice."

"Highness, Lowness, all the same to me. But being as we are old friends maybe I'll just call you Bee. If that will Bee alright, Bee. Bee anyway you wanna Bee, that's what I say."

Beatrice wondered if Bee was one of her soul names that she did not know about yet. She actually quite liked it. But then Jake began singing loudly, "Doo-Bee-Doo-Bee-Doo. Hey, nice lil' anthem that – might catch on, doncha think?"

Beatrice said nothing and tried to look dignified and horrified at the same time, as Sheba would have done. But it was all lost on Jake.

"Now that we've got that figured out, how's about a game of footie? I can teach you American footie if you like. Ball's the wrong shape, but we'll manage."

He batted a tennis ball towards her so hard that Beatrice had to jump out the way. Then it seemed only natural and polite to bat it back to him. And before long the two of them were racing around together and pouncing on each other like the old friends Jake insisted they were. Foreign he might be. Common he might be. But Beatrice couldn't remember having so much fun – ever.

* * *

"No, no, I don't believe it. It's not possible."

Beatrice froze, her head in the linen basket, where the ball had got wedged inside one of the Lady's bras. Her mother was home.

"Has there been a revolution? Have we been invaded? Is the Queendom collapsed?" Sheba's voice had the cold, controlled tone that Beatrice had come to dread.

"No, of course not. It is a Princess who has allowed this appalling state of affairs. A Princess who has overturned her own palace. A Princess who has allowed herself to play with such indignity, such abandon that the entire Queendom is reduced to chaos.

"Beatrice, what is it that I have done to deserve this? I am shocked at your behaviour and – yes, I have to say it – I am ashamed of you."

"Mummy, it wasn't just me. There was this weird black cat that got in. His name's Jake and he wouldn't go away and he made me play with him and he's over there now in that corner. Look!"

"Not just a destroyer and a commoner but a liar too."
Sheba's beautiful tail was swinging furiously and her voice
was pure ice. "There is no black cat in this room. Do you take
me for a complete fool?"

Beatrice removed her head from the basket and looked
around. Jake was nowhere to be seen. He must have escaped
down the stairs. But if he had done that then he would have
met Sheba on the way up surely?

"He was here, really Mummy. And he spoke with this
funny accent. I think maybe he was American."

"Enough! Silence!" Queen Sheba shivered in disgust. "Just
take yourself out of my sight. I am not sure that I ever wish
to see you again."

So Beatrice crawled back into the laundry basket and found
herself a nice warm place in between two jumpers and a pair
of pyjamas. Usually when Sheba shouted Beatrice wept for
hours on end. But today she still felt happy from all her playing and excited about her new friend – though he might have
done the decent thing and waited to face the music with her.
Especially since Jake had seemed to know Sheba quite well.
Maybe if he came again, she could ask him.

She began to wash herself from the top of her head to the
tip of her tail. After all, a girl needed to look good for her
admirers, especially a Princess. It was only when she came to
her belly that she realised the black bits had returned. Well,
that was a relief. Though it was all very puzzling. Markings
moving was bad enough. Markings disappearing, that was
a real mystery. And it had to be said, the bits that had returned
definitely looked a bit rough round the edges. She would need
to lick them into shape, so they'd stay put in future.

Her rough tongue flicked and rubbed rhythmically in all
directions for minutes, maybe an hour. It was only right at
the end, when the rebellious markings had become sharp and
clear and clean and she was lying back admiring her work,

that she felt something stir. She looked down at her flanks and there, deep inside one particularly glossy black patch, she thought she saw something winking at her. Impossible. She must be overtired with all the excitement of the day. But as she drifted off to sleep she thought she heard a voice speaking in her ear. A slow, soft, drawling voice.

"Bee Happy," it said.

CHAPTER 4

AN ANOMALY

Every day after that Beatrice waited for Jake to return. She looked in all the cupboards and the boxes. She listened for his voice. She climbed on the windowsills and looked out into the Wildwoods, where she was not allowed to go, but there was no sign of him anywhere.

"It's quite simple Beatrice. The person you think you met wasn't real. He is what we call an Imaginary Friend. Lots of kittens have them. Though why you should imagine an American cat I really don't know. A cat from a republic with no concept of the royal line." Sheba shivered with horror at the thought.

"So you can stop mooning around and staring at those dreadful woods. He's not coming back. I will not have a republican in my palace. Why, soon we'll be living in the Wild West. The Wildwoods are bad enough. Filthy, muddy, mucky place. Brambles and trees everywhere. Not to mention the dogs. Really this is a place of unbelievable savagery."

Queen Sheba's voice had that tone which Beatrice recognised as the beginning of a familiar litany. To relieve the boredom she began to recite along with her mother. Their voices rose together in harmonious plainchant.

That I, who am descended from the Queens of Egypt,
Whose ancestors enjoyed sand and sunshine,
Temples and pyramids,

Who ate with Pharaohs
Who slept on silk sheets…

Sheba stopped. Beatrice wondered for a moment whether she had forgotten the words. But when her mother spoke again the singsong voice had gone and the words were different. Spiky, like the Lady's cactus plant – the one with thorny bits that got stuck in Beatrice's paws.

"That I – I, a Queen – should be expected to climb trees like a monkey. Or to wallow in mud like a…like a hippo… to attend to my personal royal needs."

"Mother, what's a hippo?" This was a new addition to the traditional verses. Beatrice thought hippos sounded rather fun. But there was no stopping Sheba now.

"That I, who was worshipped by men, whose image was carved in stone for generations to behold and wonder at, should be living in a boarding house in a cold country and forced to eat meals from a packet, served on a…a saucer!"

Sheba spat out the word as though it contained poison and let out a wail so loud the vases on the shelves around began to shake. There seemed to be no particular words to the song now, so Beatrice joined in again. She liked singing. It made a change from sitting still and trying to be beautiful.

But The Lady didn't like singing. She was up the stairs faster than a rat up a drainpipe. Or maybe a hippo. Did hippos climb drainpipes, Beatrice wondered?

"Come on, you two. Stop that racket. Out of here this minute."

To Beatrice's amazement the Lady slid her hands under Sheba's royal belly and picked her up. She was so fast there was no time for the Queen to lash and slash with her claws like she usually did. The Lady knew better than to give her a cuddle, because that was when Sheba liked to turn her head and bite hard at the hand that stroked her. She simply

21

dangled Sheba in mid-air so her back legs hung down as she kicked the air, snarling and spitting. Sheba didn't look much like a Queen now, and she didn't sound like one either. So much, Beatrice thought, for Queenly Attitudes.

She listened to the sound of the Lady's heavy footsteps on the stairs. "No grace, no dignity, like a herd of elephants," Sheba always said. Beatrice had never seen an elephant though now she knew what one sounded like. But where was her mother's own grace and dignity now? She heard the kitchen door creak and then a loud thud on the path outside. Surely that couldn't be? Surely she wouldn't have? To throw Sheba out like a bag of rubbish. That anyone would dare behave towards a Queen in such a way. Let alone a servant.

Beatrice was shocked. She felt Sheba's humiliation as if it were her own. It was a strange sensation, quite unlike the Queen's anger, which was fierce and spiky and white-cold. This was sad and shaky and heavy and a sort of watery grey colour. It wasn't proud and demanding, it was dirty and disfigured. The sort of feeling that wanted to hide itself in corners, to gurgle down the drain and disappear forever.

For the first time in her life, Beatrice felt sorry for her mother. She wanted to comfort her, to cuddle up to her soft belly which smelt deliciously of wool and milk and fish paste, to lick her all over until she knew every part of her was clean and loved, that she was every inch a Queen. Of course she knew it would never happen. Sheba would return eventually – a bit colder, a bit frostier, probably even more critical – and they would never speak of it again.

Beatrice was sad about that too. Her markings began to droop with misery and slide towards the floor. She was just wondering what she could do to help when she saw a movement in the corner of the room. A rush of excitement ran up and down her spine. A mouse, perhaps? She had heard about mice, but she had never seen one. Maybe they were like

22

hippos, or perhaps elephants, though this one seemed quite small and quiet. Anyway she had better be ready.

Beatrice crouched down, with her bottom in the air and wiggled it a bit from side to side as Sheba had taught her to do. Then she kept very still and focused hard till her eyes went big and black. Yes, there was definitely something shifting around underneath an old grey dressing gown. With more glee than precision she jumped. The lump squealed.

This was fun. The more Beatrice slammed her paws down the more the lump wriggled and ran from side to side in an attempt to escape. At first she kept one paw firmly on the grey towelling and teased and tormented the mystery creature with her other paw. Eventually excitement got the better of her and she drew both paws back for The Big Pounce. But in the split second before she landed the lump managed to escape. Or part of it did. Poking out from underneath one corner of the garment she saw a tiny pink nose and a white furry face.

"Please stop," the face squeaked. "Please don't hurt me. I didn't mean no harm. I'll do anything."

"No mercy for mice," yelled Beatrice in a most unqueenly manner. She was just about to jump again when the creature let out a loud, terrified meow. Beatrice halted in mid-air and came down hard on four legs at once onto the carpet. Surely not? But, yes, this tiny white wailing thing was a kitten – the tiniest kitten Beatrice had ever seen though, come to think of it, it was also the first kitten Beatrice had ever seen, apart from herself. Using her teeth she dragged the dressing gown away and took a good long look.

Bright blue eyes regarded Beatrice with terror from a face of exquisite delicacy. The ears were clean and pink inside. Far too big for now, of course, but she would grow into them. Elsewhere the fur was long and fluffy like candyfloss. Beatrice hadn't seen candyfloss but Sheba often used the

23

word to describe herself when she had been a kitten. "Soft as a cloud, sweet as sugar, spun like silk, that was me."

The kitten's tail was still a bit stubby, but that would develop in time. And everywhere was the purest, softest white, except for the four paws, which were unaccountably black.

"I'm…I'm sorry about the paws," the creature whimpered, seeing her gaze. "I'm sorry…about everything."

"That's alright," said Beatrice, "I have the same problem with my own markings sometimes." But then she looked down at her paws and was surprised to find that for once they were completely white.

"Anyhow, black paws don't show the dirt," she told the kitten in what she hoped was a kindly and reassuring manner.

"It's alright for you," said the kitten. "But I'm supposed to be pedigree."

Beatrice experienced a flash of irritation. Who did this little upstart think she was?

"Well, I am supposed to be a Princess, actually," she said haughtily. "No, I *am* a Princess. And I can assure you my bloodline is faultless, so I would remind you that you are a guest in this palace. And an uninvited one at that."

"Oooh dear. Oooh no, I've done it again," the kitten wailed. "I didn't mean no offence."

"*Any* offence," Beatrice interjected, sounding remarkably like her mother.

"*Any* offence," the kitten repeated. "See what I mean? I can't get nothing right. That's why I ran away. And now I have nobody. No home, no friends. And now you don't like me neither." She lifted up the corner of the dressing gown and tried to crawl back underneath.

"Oh no you don't." Beatrice reached out her paw and dragged the kitten back out again. She rolled her over so she lay on her back with her little belly exposed. It was pumping up and down with fear. "What do they call you anyway?"

"I…I'm not sure. I think my name's Nomaly. Soon as I was born they said I was a Nomaly. And that means I'm all wrong and so they won't be able to show me or nothing. And cos I'm no use they were going to give me away or take me to the pet shop."

Nomaly's voice became higher and higher and squeakier and squeakier till Beatrice thought her ears would explode.

"Stop that wailing. Stop it at once!"

The command came out so sharply that Beatrice thought Sheba must be in the room and turned round cowering a little. Then she realised, with horror, that she had said the words herself. Still, they seemed to have worked. Little Nomaly had stopped wailing and just looked frozen with terror. She spoke more kindly:

"How did you get here anyway?"

"I…I don't know. I think maybe I got lost and hid in the basket and then I fell asleep. And I just woke up here. But there was all that noise going on and that very scary big cat was here so I didn't dare come out."

Beatrice smiled. "Well, that might have been a wise decision. That was my mother, Queen Sheba." Suddenly Beatrice remembered something her mother had said. Her eyes narrowed. "I've never heard of a cat being called Nomaly. You sure you didn't steal it?"

"Wh…what d'you mean?" Nomaly's blue eyes were wide with terror. Then Beatrice realised that actually she herself had no idea what she meant at all either.

"Never mind," she said more kindly. "But you must have another name. Most cats have several.

"I, for instance, am Her Royal Highness the Princess Beatrice of the Wildwoods. And now I am also called Bee, though I have never told anyone else that." Beatrice smiled at the memories of that surprising afternoon. "Anyway, you are so cute you deserve a nice name."

She nuzzled the kitten's tiny, round belly. Now she was close up she could see it was actually a bit grubby. She gave a quick lick for good measure. "I know, let's call you Candy, because you look like candyfloss."

"What's candyfloss?"

"It's soft as a cloud, sweet as sugar, spun like silk," said Beatrice, knowledgeably and without hesitation.

"Oh, that's nice. But does it have black boots?"

Beatrice sighed. This was going to be hard work. "I know, let's play a game. What games do you know?"

Candy looked anxious. "Pedigrees don't play."

"Well neither do Princesses. But we are allowed to develop Special Skills. So let's see how many things you can do with this." She swiped the lager bottle top across the carpet. "I call it the Ten Top Talents challenge."

So for the next hour Beatrice schooled her little friend in Pouncing, Carrying, Kicking, Hiding, Juggling, Balancing (on the head), Lifting (single paw only), Throwing, Rolling and finally Sticking. This last one involved sticking the bottle top on your nose and keeping it there while walking backwards. Beatrice wasn't sure when she would ever use this particular skill but it was the most fun so she always finished off with it anyway – as long as Sheba wasn't looking.

At the end of it little Candy was so tired she just curled up in a ball and fell fast asleep. Beatrice sat for a while watching her. It was good to have someone to play with and to look after. But Candy was little and she really should be going home now, though it didn't sound like home was much fun. If only she could help.

Then Beatrice had an idea. It might not work, but Candy was asleep anyway, so she would never know. Very gently she passed her tongue over one of the four sooty black feet.

"Please," she pleaded silently, "please help. Do as I ask."

She licked very softly, over and over and eventually she

felt the tiniest release. Yes, the black was letting go. Carefully, she swept her tongue up Candy's front leg. The black fur moved with her. Don't stop now or she'll end up with a black shoulder. Past the shoulder and neck, over the face, holding her breath, all the way to the nose. And…relax. There they were – the tiniest delicate markings around the nose. She flicked with her tongue to feather them out a bit. Purrfect.

Next she did the ears. Back down to the second paw and up with the black over the lovely white flanks to make one beautiful black tipped ear. The third paw did the second ear and then it was just the tail remaining. As the black from the last paw moved up Candy's haunches and along her stubby kitten tail to the very tip, the white fur slid and settled so the four paws became clean and white. By the end the sleeping Candy had an exquisite black-tipped tail, two gorgeous black-tipped ears and the cutest, tiniest black-tipped nose Beatrice had ever seen. And everywhere else was purest white. In fact she looked for all the world like a miniature version of Queen Sheba herself.

Candy had turned into a proper pedigree kitten and a real show-stopper. Her family would not recognise her. A pity Beatrice could not manage her own markings as easily as she could manage Candy's. In any case there would be no more talk of pet shops for sure. Beatrice could not wait for her friend to wake up and see the transformation, but just now she felt very tired after all her hard work. She curled herself around Candy and settled down to sleep, imagining herself wrapped in a white blanket with four neat black corners where nothing moved and everything was safe. But sleep was a long time coming. Because behind her closed lids she saw not the sweet little Candy, the kitten of her own creation, but the great Queen Sheba, cold and angry and humiliated. Alone in the wild Wildwoods.

CHAPTER 5

GOING OUT

It was dark when Beatrice woke, aware of a gnawing emptiness in her belly that did not feel like hunger. She looked down to check that her markings were all still there but for once everything seemed to be in order. Sheba would be pleased. But Sheba had still not returned after the terrible humiliations of the day before. Beatrice felt unaccountably anxious. Her mother went out on her own at other times, sometimes staying away for long periods, though she always refused to say where she had been. But this time something was different. Seeing the great Queen so vulnerable had been a shock for Beatrice. It was as though the world had tipped over on its axis like a great big cardboard box and everything had fallen out. Nowhere felt safe anymore.

Then she remembered Candy, her little kitten visitor from the night before. Where could she be? Surely she could not have been a dream? Beatrice checked under the blankets and searched in the laundry basket. But Candy was definitely gone. Had she made her way down the stairs and out through the little door that Sheba called the portcullis and the Lady called the cat flap? And if so, how would she find her path home?

Candy was just a tiny kitten and the Great Outdoors could be dangerous. Indeed Beatrice, who was considerably older than Candy, wasn't allowed out yet. She felt worried for her new friend and sad to have lost her so soon. But maybe she would come back to visit again. Beatrice smiled to think how amazed Candy's family would be to see her returning as a proper pedigree. Perhaps they would be nicer to her now and even give her a decent name instead of that silly Nomaly. Perhaps they wouldn't even recognise her at all.

She looked around. Without Candy or Sheba the attic felt big and lonely and very dark. Usually the only time Sheba stayed out at night was when the moon was round and full.

"There she hangs, like an opal in indigo," she would sigh, looking up through the attic window, her back arching and stretching, her whole body consumed by longing.

"She calls to me and who can resist? There is no gainsaying such beauty on such a night. I must leave all for this call. Farewell, my dear…until we meet again!"

And off she would go as if drawn by a magnet, as if Beatrice and the Lady and the attic meant nothing to her at all.

Beatrice had never seen an opal and she could not hear anyone calling. Actually, she thought the moon looked like one of those silvery baubles in the Christmas decoration box. But what did it matter? Tonight there was no moon and there were no stars either. The sky was not indigo, it was low and black. The rain, which had been tapping gently on the attic windows was starting to hammer on them instead and the wind soared and howled in the eaves. Strange shrieks came from the Wildwoods. Beatrice's markings huddled together in fear. Where was Sheba? And where was Candy? Should she go and look for them? Beatrice liked to sit and look out of the big glass windows but she was still too scared to actually want to go outside. The Great Outdoors could be a dangerous place, full of all sorts of strange creatures. Sheba often talked with horror of the dogs that bounded through the Wildwoods with murderous intent. Beatrice had only seen one – a huge, hairy thing which had chased Sheba right up the garden path and only stopped when she was safely through the cat flap.

It had stayed there, jumping and barking, for at least ten minutes until its red-faced owner had appeared.

At night the dogs went home but the foxes came out, as well as huge bear-like creatures with stripy faces. Beatrice had never seen a bear or a fox but she imagined them like the enormous shadows that sometimes appeared on the attic walls as well as in her dreams. What if one of them had caught Sheba or Candy and eaten them? The thought of such horrors sent her markings plummeting towards the floor. Some of them even tried to crawl away over the carpet but, after her success with Candy, Beatrice was better prepared.

"No you don't." She put out a paw and trapped them neatly. The culprits – two big patches of white and gold – reversed reluctantly back into position. "Tonight you do as I say for once."

Beatrice put her nose through the attic door and listened carefully. A rhythmic snoring told her the Lady was asleep. She padded downstairs, past the bedroom and down another set of stairs into the kitchen. This was where Beatrice and Sheba dined twice daily. There was also a special tray where Beatrice did her Unmentionables until she was big enough to do them outside. Her mother had explained that one of the Lady's most important duties was to be Keeper of the Royal Stool. This was a great honour for a courtier, though from the fuss the Lady made about it some days you could be forgiven for imagining it was actually a punishment. The tray was nice and clean so Beatrice did a quick Unmentionable. It was satisfyingly smelly and she covered it up neatly as a game for the Lady to find in the morning before heading over to the cat flap.

Beatrice had seen Sheba come in and out many times, so she knew how it worked. She put a paw up against the flap and pushed. Nothing. She tried two paws at a time. That didn't work either. She tried to nudge it open with her head but she was too little and she could not apply enough pressure. Then she decided to take a run at it from the other side of the kitchen, but after a dozen wild charges she just ended up with a very sore head. She was sitting looking at it in despair when all of the sudden the flap started to move of its own accord.

"Mummy?" shouted Beatrice, "is that you?"

But she could see nothing in the darkness outside. The flap moved again. Her markings shivered with fear. Then a single black paw appeared with huge sharp claws. SOMETHING WAS COMING IN. A bear? A herd of elephants? She felt her colours beginning to slide off, but she was too frightened to call them back. She tried to hide but when she looked down there was nothing of herself left to hide. It was like she wasn't there at all.

Most of the markings had crawled away into secret spots. Some had tried to camouflage themselves among the black boots. Others were pretending to be cushions on the rocking chair. And the white ones had flattened themselves up against the washing machine in an attempt to make themselves invisible. She had to admit it, those white patches might be badly behaved and cowardly, but they could also be pretty clever at times. Then it occurred to her, if her markings were all over the place, where exactly did that leave her? Her tummy had turned somersaults and seemed to have disappeared into the cushions as well. She couldn't feel her legs, just a sort of jelly-like quaking where they used to be. And when she looked she couldn't see them either. All she could see of herself was a sort of vague outline, like a drawing that needed to be coloured in. Where was she? And who was she without them?

Before she could address this philosophical issue a voice spoke from the other side – a voice she recognised.

"Hey Bee. That you making all that racket? What's up? You fancy a night out on the town? Or should I say a night out in the woods? Heh heh!"

She recognised the familiar chuckle. "Jake?"

"At your service ma'am. What would your pleasure be, Bee?"

"Oh, I am so glad you are here. I've lost my mother? And I've lost Candy?"

"Well, that's very careless of you. How careless can you be, Bee? Heh, heh!"

"Stop it. This is serious."

"Begging your pardon ma'am. Don't mean no offence."

Despite his words and his bad grammar and his impudent tone Beatrice was too pleased to see him to object.

"Now that old lag Sheba I know of course, but who is this Candy? She sounds the sort of sweet little creature I could just do with getting to know."

"Candy's only a kitten, but she's so cute and she's gone somewhere and I don't know where she came from or where she's going to."

"Hey kid, none of us know that."

"And actually, Sheba says she doesn't know you at all. In fact she says you are – what was it again? – that's right – you are a Figment. Of my imagination. Which means I've made you up. Which means you don't exist. So there."

From the other side of the cat flap came a loud roar of laughter.

"All I can say, girl, is you've got one hell of an imagination. So if I don't exist, then I am not really holding open this darn cat flap and you are not really going to come through. And there's not really anything to be frightened of. So what are we waiting for?"

Actually Beatrice was waiting for her markings but she wasn't going to tell Jake that. They were slinking back across the kitchen floor towards her looking a little shamefaced. She decided to play for time.

"Umm I've never been outside before."

32

"That so? Well these black bits seem pretty sure of themselves."

Beatrice looked down. Not only had her front legs gone completely black but some of the black patches had passed her by and were already sliding through the narrow gap in the cat flap created by Jake's paw.

"I wouldn't let them go out on their own in this weather, Bee. You might never see them again."

Jake gave another infuriating chuckle. Beatrice put her nose to the open cat flap. The scent of woods at night rushed into her nostrils and made her feel lightheaded. The next moment, to her surprise, the wandering markings swerved back on themselves and settled decisively on her head so that her face, her ears, her chest and front legs were as black as the night outside and she hardly showed up at all. The disguise made her feel strong and confident for the first time. There was no doubt about it, her head wanted to go out. The trouble was that the rest of her was stuck.

Out of the corner of her eye she could see that her body was now arranged in a series of stripes. Her head and front paws, which were outside the cat flap, were black. Her middle, which was half in and half out, was pure gold. And inside the kitchen her bottom, back legs and tail were completely white.

"I'm sorry, Jake, I can't go out looking like this."

Jake moved to the side so he had a better view through the glass. "Hey Bee you've turned into a humbug." His laughter crackled in the darkness till Beatrice thought she could see sparks flying.

"It's not funny!" Beatrice tried to move but her cowardly white back legs seemed to be stuck to the floor.

"Humbugs always were sticky sweets. Guess that's what you get for playing with Candy." Jake was so pleased with his joke that he rolled over and over on the patio, stretching his long legs and displaying his big round belly.

Beatrice felt cross, very cross indeed. So cross that a funny, shaky feeling began building up inside her. She was cross with the Lady for throwing Sheba out and with Sheba for not coming home. She was cross with Candy for leaving. She was cross with Jake for laughing. But most of all she was furious with her markings for their cowardice and for humiliating her in front of him.

"Glad to see at least the black bits are behaving. No black marks for the black marks eh?" Jake eyed his own coat appreciatively. "Seems like they've got a spirit of adventure. Like yours truly, of course. But as for the rest…"

He shook his head in such a patronising way that Beatrice thought she would explode with rage. She began to shake with fury from the tip of her shiny black nose to the end of her rebellious white tail. As she trembled and shook the gold fur rubbed back and forth against the frame of the cat flap.

"That's my girl. If the white don't move, try the gold. There's always a way. That white stuff can be real stubborn. You have to be a bit sneaky. Kind of take it by surprise. Now come on baby, shake your stuff. Bit at a time. Make like you're one of those champagne corks old Sheba keeps on about coming out of the bottle. That's right." He gave a huge whoop of amusement and delight.

Beatrice had been paralysed by her own anger as well as by the behaviour of her markings, but now she saw what Jake was talking about. She could not stay here all night. She had to move in one direction or another. Clearly the black parts had no intention of staying inside tonight and the white did not want to leave the cosy kitchen. If she could just get the gold parts of her moving where she wanted then the white would have to follow, surely? Otherwise she would still be here, stuck half in and half out of the flap when the Lady came down for breakfast in the morning. The thought of such shame set the shaking off even more. But, thinking about

34

what Jake said, this time she would not fight it. Instead, she gave herself up to it entirely. She let it take over her whole being. The vibrations grew inside her and outside her, stronger and stronger and louder and louder until they felt like one enormous purr, which was remarkably pleasant. Jake started singing loudly – as loudly as Sheba and almost as badly.

"Go for it Bay-Bee. Let it go...let it go!"

So Beatrice gave herself up to the singing and the shaking and the giant purr till she wobbled and trembled like a stripy blancmange. As each new wave passed through her body she stretched her black paws and her head a little further outside. And each time the gold markings moved forward just a few inches, pulling the white ones reluctantly behind them, till her back legs were standing on tiptoe. Eventually she had pushed herself so far through the opening that there was more of her outside than in. Beatrice waited for the next wave of shivering to begin and just as it reached its peak she threw herself forward in a really big dive. She felt her back paws and claws tear from the wooden kitchen floor and clatter through the cat flap behind her onto the stone patio. She had done it. She was in the Great Outdoors.

CHAPTER 6
THE GREAT OUTDOORS

The first thing Beatrice noticed was that the Great Outdoors was much greater than she could ever have imagined. It was one thing to look at it through the big glass windows. It was another altogether to be in it, to be a part of it. It seemed to go on forever – as far as she could see and a great deal further. There were trees and paths and bushes and walls. But the walls were so low they did not actually make her feel safe because anyone could jump over them with a little effort.

Weirdest of all, there was no ceiling. There was just the sky that went on and on, like the biggest emptiness Beatrice had ever imagined and then bigger still. The moon, which had looked quite large when it peeked through the attic window, was now no more than a speck of silver dust behind the scudding clouds.

The rain was different too. She had watched rain from inside and liked the way it pattered gently against the stone slabs on the patio or jabbed at the windows furiously, like a million claws coming down at once. The noise made it even more exciting. But it was quite another matter to be actually outside in it. Now the water poured down onto her black head and her golden back and her white bottom, sticking her fur together and sliding through the gaps till she could feel its coolness on her skin. And beneath her carefully washed paws, the ground was dissolving into sticky mud.

The wind was another mystery. Up in the attic Beatrice had thought of the wind as a friend – a noisy, rumbustious one that wrapped itself around the house and sang and whistled or moaned sadly, depending on what mood it was in. But now, in the Great Outdoors, it seemed the wind was not a real person at all, just an emptiness that moved every which way. One minute it whispered in the huge trees so they had to bow their heads to listen. The next it tickled Beatrice's markings and blew them up the wrong way. But when she turned her head to remonstrate with it, there was no one there at all.

"Don't touch me!" Beatrice spoke loudly to it, to show she was not afraid. But the wind just whipped round and blew some more rain across her face. It was cold and icy.

She jumped up on all fours and turned around just in time to see a white flash. That must be the wind, she thought. She would catch it and show it a thing or two. She grabbed at it with her paws, but as fast as she moved, it disappeared. She tried again and again, turning circle after circle until she was too dizzy to go on and had to lie down on the wet stone to catch her breath. Beneath her she could feel her markings grimacing in distaste. Then she noticed something white and furry flicking angrily at her rear end and realised that she had been wasting her efforts chasing her own tail. Meanwhile the wind itself had disappeared like a coward – if something that is invisible to start with can actually be said to disappear.

Out of the darkness a large black shape loomed. Quick as a flash Beatrice's markings did an about turn, so her head turned white and her bottom went black. True to form, the white parts raced towards the safety of the cat flap. Her front paws were just pushing it open when the shape jumped on her, grabbing her bottom and back legs so she couldn't move.

Her heart was beating so loudly she didn't even hear the voice at first, but then she recognised a familiar chuckle.

"Let me go, Jake. I'm too little. It's too big. I want to go home."

"Now don't be a baby, Baybee."

Then, horror of horrors, she felt his teeth sink into the white fur at the back of her head. The next thing, Jake had actually picked her up by the scruff of her neck, just like Sheba had done when she was a tiny kitten.

"Put me down, put me down this instant."

"Well, my dear," Jake's mouth was rather full of her fur so he had to speak out of the side of his mouth, making his drawl even more peculiar, "if you wanna behave like a baby, well, then I'm gonna treat you like one."

"I'm not a baby, I'm a Princess!" Beatrice squealed. But no sound came out. With Jake's teeth holding tightly to the back of her neck, her head hung at such an angle that she couldn't make a sound. The squeal was all inside her head.

The cloud parted and for a few moments the wet woods sparkled in the moonlight. Beneath her, Beatrice's legs dangled, white and black, and her golden belly glistened with raindrops.

"You wanna find that snobby old dame Sheba, we're gonna find her. And I have to say I'm just in the mood for a piece of Candy."

Beatrice's spine, hanging from Jake's mouth, tingled with shame and fear and another emotion she didn't quite recognise which caused her black tail to twitch wildly. Candy was *her* friend. She did not want to share her with anyone, especially with an uncouth republican with a common accent. But she was too tired and too little to struggle against him.

She closed her eyes and allowed her body to go limp. The night air rushed to greet her with its cocktail of scents. Sheba had often described to her the musty aroma of decaying leaves, and the metallic tones of wet rock covered in moss and lichen. "Far from the sacred oils to which I am accustomed but charming in their way, though the moulds do little for my digestion." But the reality was overwhelming.

Carried on the air, from near and far, came the sweetness of sheep and the powerful musk of the wild. Beatrice could distinguish some smells – the peaty damp earth, the fresh wet grass and the sharp, green odour of ferns. In between these, woven in and out like threads in a tapestry, were a thousand other unfamiliar scents – plants and places and strange creatures to be discovered. To be hunted or to be feared.

When she opened her eyes, they had left the gardens far behind and the little house was out of sight. Around her the tree trunks rose like pillars. Their leaves covered the sky so that Beatrice couldn't see its foreverness. That made her feel a bit safer, almost like being in the attic. She sensed her markings beginning to relax a little. In front of her, great stone slabs rose up and then dropped away sharply. She felt Jake's head lower and his jaws loosen as he put her down softly on a wet patch of soil.

"Hey BayBee, welcome to the Wildwoods. Now ain't that just *wild*?"

It was too wild for Beatrice. No sooner had her paws touched the ground than she dived beneath Jake and hid herself amid the folds of his belly. She breathed in the smell of him – grass and wood smoke and something surprisingly fresh, like a mixture of lavender and pine needles.

"Hey now, don't wriggle so. You're tickling me." Jake's chuckle made her feel a little safer.

"It's natural for a young girl like you to be a little scared the first time. But, y'know Bee, you should be excited, cos from what you told me the other day, this here's your very own Queendom – or it will be one day. So why don't you come out now and at least take a look at it?"

Her Queendom. Who wanted a Queendom anyway? What was wrong with an attic? Nevertheless, Beatrice removed her head from Jake's nether regions and wriggled around slowly, never taking her belly off the ground. Once she was facing outwards she managed to sit upright so that her white upper body lay back against Jake's chest. His paws guarded her safely in front and her gold bits disappeared into the blackness where his belly met her black bottom and tail. From a distance they could have been one large black cat with a white bib. Despite Jake's lamentable lack of respect and his appalling behaviour, Beatrice felt very safe and protected.

"See, kid? Now that's not so bad is it? You and me, we'll just stay like this for a bit while you git your bearings. Now, you see this here big slab of stone next to us?" He gestured with his tail. "This is the edge of what's called the quarry. That's a sort of massive hole left where people have taken stone out to make houses and patios and stuff."

"And palaces?" asked Beatrice.

"If that's what that mad dame would have you believe, then yes. In fact I did hear some of this stone is now in Buckingham Palace itself."

"Where's Buckingham Palace? Not in the Wildwoods? They're not the people who've stolen the Queendom are they? Am I going to have to fight them to get it back?"

"I certainly hope not, there's a few more of them than there are of you. And I did hear they've got a deadly pack of corgis. Anyhow don't you worry about that now, little one, they are a long way away. What you need to know is that this here quarry's full of caves and holes and secret passages. Great hunting country, running with rats and mice and rabbits. Worth remembering if ever you get hungry and you need something in a hurry. Very tasty."

Jake started to salivate at the thought of all the great suppers he had enjoyed there over the years. Two large drops of saliva dribbled onto the top of Beatrice's head. She shook them off.

"And are there bears too and elephants? Can you catch them, Jake?"

Jake threw back his head and roared with laughter. "Well now, there ain't nothing to stop you hunting them, but you ain't going to find them here. Biggest thing we've got is the

40

badgers. See those big holes over there? That's where Badger City begins. Huge tunnels, going on for miles all underneath this wood. Big as your Queendom, I shouldn't wonder. But that's top secret of course. Badgers, they're real special. We don't tell no one about them."

"Why, will they eat us?" Beatrice's markings began to curl up into little balls of fear.

"Well now I never knowed 'em eat a cat. Funny thing is they're so big and powerful, the most powerful thing I ever did see, 'cept maybe the brown bears back home. But mostly they eat worms and hedgehogs and little stuff."

Beatrice wondered what a worm was, but didn't like to ask.

"Still, they can pack a punch, I don't mind telling you. You see one, you be respectful now Bee. Wouldn't want to end up on the wrong side of them, that's for sure."

That's rich, thought Beatrice, Jake telling anyone else to be respectful. But she did not say anything. Anyway Candy was very respectful so if she had got lost down here she probably would not upset the badgers.

"Are we going in the quarry now?"

"I don't reckon that's where old Sheba will be tonight. 'Sides, I think it's probably a bit much for you, first night out an' all. You reckon you can walk a bit now?"

Beatrice nodded, though her head was beneath Jake's so he couldn't actually see it.

"Well now, you just follow me. Anything you want to know, just ask. But you get scared, just don't go haring off anywhere by yourself."

Jake sounded quite protective – like a proper courtier. They walked together through the Wildwoods. Beatrice stayed very close to Jake and just a little bit behind him so she could hide if she needed to. Bit by bit her heart stopped thumping and she started to notice all the new things outside of her instead of the old fears inside.

They padded along the side of the great quarry, keeping an eye out all the time for foxes and badgers and rats and worms. Beatrice especially wanted to see a worm because she had never heard of them before and couldn't imagine what one looked like. They walked along one muddy path, and then another muddy path and then through thick grass until they came to a rocky outcrop.

"Nearly there. Keep quiet now, Bee, we don't want to disturb them."

"Disturb who?" said Beatrice loudly, but Jake just hushed her and jumped onto an overhanging ledge and then up again till he was right above her.

"Up you come now, Bee. Think you can make it?"

Beatrice took a big jump but just missed the overhang and ended up sliding down the rock face on her bottom. She tried again, but this time she turned right over in a somersault and landed flat on her back. It would have been quite fun if it hadn't been so undignified and if Jake would only wipe that stupid, patronising grin off his face. Then she noticed a path to the side which came out right on top of the rock where Jake sat – what Sheba would call the Path of Least Resistance. Easy-peasy. He might have told her about it. Doubtless he had just been showing off with all that jumping.

She padded gently up the path and sat down next to him. Before them was a large clearing covered in grass and soft moss. In the centre was a huge standing stone. In front of that stone was Sheba. And in front of Sheba, Beatrice was amazed to see Candy.

"Bee-a-utiful, very bee-a-utiful. Quite exquisite, really."

At first Beatrice thought Sheba was talking to herself as usual. Then she realised she was talking to Candy. About Candy.

"I…I do my best, Ma'am."

Candy was sitting facing Sheba. Her markings were still perfectly correct, just as Beatrice had left them. She looked in fact like a miniature version of the great Queen herself.

"I only wish my own daughter could begin to manage her markings the way you do, my dear. My Beatrice, well, she has spirit but really that's all I can say for her, I'm afraid. Of course there's potential there. But with all those colours…." Sheba shook her head and her voice faded away tragically. "All I can say is, I hold out very little hope."

"Beatrice?" Candy's voiced trembled. "Did you say Beatrice is your daughter?"

"Sadly, my dear, yes. Not that I don't love her, of course. One is a mother after all. But a kitten like you – well, my dear, there's a soul connection. I'm sure you can feel it."

"B…but Beatrice is my f…f…friend. She made me beautiful. She made me into a p…p…proper p…pedigree."

"Now then dear, don't tell fibs. You are only little and you are very beautiful so I will make allowances on this occasion. But Beatrice never goes anywhere, so you can't possibly have met her. Of course I tell her she's not allowed out because she's too young, but truthfully I really don't feel I can let her be seen in public. Certainly not at the moment."

Beatrice could not believe her snowy white ears, or her gold ones, or her black ones for that matter, as the shock caused her markings to swap over, one after the other. That her mother could be so treacherous and so unkind! That she would prefer Candy to her own daughter – and even lie about why Beatrice had not gone out before.

"Don't believe her Candy, it's not true," she shouted. But the wind took her words and blew them way up into the endless sky where they escaped.

"You are a traitor and you will be executed!" Beatrice stamped her four little paws one after the other on the soft grass. But this time the rain came back and washed her words right into the earth.

"I hate you," she screamed. "You stupid, poncy pedigrees, with your prissy long fur that never gets dirty and your pathetic points of black that never do anything. You may think you are perfect now but just wait till I'm Queen. Things will be different, believe me!"

She spat the words out of her mouth like bullets. But this time an enormous winged creature swooped down from the trees behind her and ate them up before they could hit their target. Beatrice dived under Jake's belly, trembling with fear and rage and the terrible sadness of betrayal.

"Hey, hey, little one," Jake's voice was soft and gentle, "don't you go scaring yourself. That there's an owl. Name of George. Nice old bird if ever there was one – as long as you're not scrapping with him over a mouse that is. Probably best he eats your words now, rather than you having to eat them later. That's the way I look at it."

"But you heard her. She thinks I'm ugly and stupid and not fit to be let out. And she wants Candy instead of me."

Jake had a rather strange expression on his face, all sort of screwed up and grumpy. The truth, which he was hiding from Beatrice, was that he was angry with Sheba for being so snobbish, and angry with himself for bringing little Beatrice into the wood in the first place where she could hear such nonsense. But he was also trying not to laugh because Beatrice's markings had now mixed themselves up so much with all the upset that she did indeed look most peculiar. There were spots and stripes and splodges everywhere. And on her face two little white patches hung from her eyes, like teardrops.

"Why now, I'm not sure she actually said that exactly, Bee. But the way I see it, if those two want to spend all day looking at each other or staring in the mirror admiring their own pedigrees, why, that's their loss. They'll never get beyond themselves. Or over themselves, for that matter."

He paused to laugh at his own joke.

"Whereas you, Bee, why you are just full of endless possibilities. You ain't even begun to explore them yet."

44

"Really?" Beatrice lifted her head, which had been hanging in shame and looked at him gratefully, though she had no idea what he was talking about. To her surprise Jake bent down and licked her face with his rough tongue till the white teardrops had moved all the way down to her paws and no longer looked like they were crying.

"Sure thing Bee. That's better. Now how about I draw you a smiley face?"

The next thing, Jake had whipped his paw round behind her head and picked out some fine black fur which he dragged to the corners of her mouth. Then he spent a minute or two grooming and tweaking them until they turned happily upwards. Beatrice couldn't actually see what he was doing but she could feel it. And despite everything – despite the wind and the rain and the scary sky and her mother's betrayal – she found she couldn't help but smile. It was most peculiar.

"That's my girl."

Beatrice was just about to retort that she was nobody's girl but everybody's Princess when her mouth began twitching uncontrollably and she let out an extremely loud, extremely deep, extremely unladylike belly-laugh. In the clearing Sheba and Candy stopped admiring each other and ran for cover, fearing there was a wild animal on the loose. This made Beatrice laugh even more. And, of course, Jake joined in.

When they had managed to catch their breath at last Jake gave her an enormous wink. "See what I mean about possibilities? All we needed to do was to draw those markings into a smile, an' just see what fun we had. Scared ol' Sheba good and proper. Just think what else we can do now. Why, I think you an' me, we should have a little party to celebrate, don't you?"

"How can we have a party when there's only two of us?"

Jake laughed. "Well, as I said just now, there are all sorts of possibilities. Come with me and I'll show you. Now do you wanna walk or would you like a lift?"

Beatrice thought about it and realised that she was very tired. It was late and she walked a long way and had a lot of excitement, after all.

"I think I'd like a lift, if you don't mind."

"Fine by me, girl."

And he took her very gently by the scruff of her neck and carried her off. This time Beatrice found she quite enjoyed the swinging motion and, in any case, however hard she tried and however upset she felt about Sheba, those markings Jake had drawn on her face just kept smiling. Beatrice had never felt so happy. Could it be that simple?

CHAPTER 7
PARTY TIME

"So here you are, Your Bee-ness. Home again."

Jake put her down carefully on the stone slabs outside the cat flap. Beatrice could feel the place on the back of her neck where Jake's teeth had gripped her, firmly but gently. She shook herself from head to toe to let the rain out. It made a shower, like a rain firework. Meanwhile her markings took advantage of the opportunity to rearrange themselves. This time they marched up and down for a few minutes like soldiers before settling back into a series of herring-bone stripes.

Jake looked at her admiringly. "Hey Bee, that what you little Englanders call the Trooping of the Colour?"

It was nice to find someone who appreciated her moveable markings instead of criticising them all the time the way Sheba did. Jake made them seem like fun instead of like a terrible mistake. Endless possibilities, she repeated to herself inwardly. She wasn't at all sure what it meant, but just the words themselves made her feel strong and confident. She pushed the cat flap open with her head, just like a proper grown-up cat.

"Are you coming in?" she asked shyly.

Beatrice was not quite sure what the protocol was for inviting people into the royal household, but she was sure there was one and that Sheba knew about it.

"Well I don't know how you're going to manage a party without me." Jake squeezed his bulky belly through with some difficulty. "Race you upstairs!"

The pair ran as fast as they could up the stairs. Beatrice, being younger and lighter, was the first to reach the attic. It seemed very small and safe after the Great Outdoors. She could hear the wind outside, howling to be allowed in. In the end it got so cross at being shut out it started throwing roof tiles and garden furniture about in frustration. Beatrice felt quite sorry for it, having to stay outside in all that rain while they were inside in the warm, even though it had been remarkably rude earlier in the evening. But Jake's mind was on more festive matters.

"Now then, let's get this party started. Your High Royalness, would you do me the honour of this dance?"

Beatrice markings bristled with irritation. Either Jake was incapable of learning royal protocol or he was doing it deliberately. She turned from the window and was just about to point out to him the error of his ways when she saw, to her amazement, that he was standing right up on his hind legs. Not only that, he was actually bowing, very elegantly, like a proper courtier. Her markings were so overcome with emotion that they transformed into a rather fetching tweed check, so she decided to overlook his impudence.

"But Jake, how can we dance when there's no music?"

Beatrice knew about parties and balls because Sheba had told her all about them. Sheba's parties had always involved the finest musicians and the best singers and the most exquisite dancers, of course.

"Hey Bee, I'm surprised at you. Only someone with no music in their soul would ask that. And I'm sure that's not you.

"Why you just listen to that rain. It's the best percussion there is. And the wind's singing along just like a violin. When it's not crashing about like a giant drum set that is. Besides, we can always make a bit of music of our own too. Nothing like a bit of bluegrass in the Wildwoods!"

Jake gave a huge whoop and a whistle and slapped his thighs in a hearty manner. Then, without even asking permission, he picked Beatrice up in his teeth again and whirled her about the room. Round and round they went, rising and falling in hypnotic rhythm while the little attic room danced round in the opposite direction. When he put her down at last she felt quite giddy and had to lie down for a little while with her paws over her eyes until the room had stopped its polka. Who knew that rooms could dance all on their own? Sheba had never taught her that.

Eventually her breathing slowed and Jake showed her how to stand on two legs herself by putting her front paws high up against the wall. For a while they practised together, side by side, stepping in and out and right and left till Jake decided it was time for Beatrice let go of the wall altogether.

"Easy-peasy, like riding a bike," he said.

"I can't ride a bike," retorted Beatrice.

"Come to think of it, neither can I," Jake chortled. "But there's plenty of time yet, I guess. Anyhow you can always catch a hold of me, Bee. Girl like you can press paws with me anytime."

And so Beatrice put up her dainty front paws (the tweed checks had transformed into pretty polka dots, like a proper party dress) and placed them against Jake's big black ones and they started to dance together properly.

They stepped forward and back. They moved sideways and round and round. They jumped up and down on the spot. Beatrice followed everything Jake did until it seemed like they moved as one person, not two. Sometimes they stepped apart from each other and Beatrice was delighted to find she could balance alone. At other times they went down on all fours and arched their backs, or did a sideways sally with their tails huge and vertical, all the time fixing each other with a ferocious stare. Then a softness came from nowhere and they linked tails and pranced up and down the room. It was very strange. Beatrice could not see any musicians, yet she could hear in her head the sound of fiddlers and drums and even the occasional flute. Was that what Jake meant by having music in your soul? Did he hear it too?

With every move she made, Beatrice felt her markings move too. But now she was not frightened or ashamed of them, rather the opposite. They curled and swayed with the music in a way that felt fluid and free and quite wonderful.

"Time to dozey-do," Jake yelled, and started circling her, encouraging her to do the same. She stepped backwards and forwards with growing confidence, though walking backwards was quite a new experience. Occasionally she missed her step and got cross with herself and her markings were thrown into confusion. When she got her rhythm back and managed to raise her eyes from her paws, she got rather a shock. Because the cat dancing opposite her was not Jake but a different cat altogether. This one was lean and muscled with eyes of the most extraordinary emerald green. Not only that, his coat was burnished gold.

"Jake?" she gasped.

"At your service, ma'am." But the familiar voice came from the corner of the room. She turned to see that Jake had found the battered guitar and was playing with the strings.

"No need to panic, Bee. This here's my friend Rufus – or Roof, as I like to call him seeing as he likes to be on top of things. Now old Roof's quite a mover so I thought maybe it was time for a little rock 'n roll?"

And he struck a loud chord on the guitar strings. The stranger gave an elegant half bow and flicked his long golden tail.

"Delighted to meet you Your Royal Highness." The new cat's voice was mellow and modulated. He had an air of distinction about him and an accent which Sheba would have described approvingly as educated.

"As my friend here said, the name's Rufus." He paused, clearly for some sort of dramatic effect. "Red Rufus. But please, do call me Roof."

Beatrice tried to smile at the new arrival but for some reason she found it almost impossible to look at him. He was just too bright – it was like looking directly into the sun. She could not for the life of her think why he was called Red, when he was pure gold.

"If you would do me the honour, Your Royal Highness."

This golden creature was actually bowing to her. By now Beatrice was finding it rather hard to stand, because her legs had gone all weak and wobbly. Thankfully, there was no time to talk before the music started up. And this time it definitely wasn't all in her head. Jake was singing.

Well it's one for the pussy
Two for the mouse
Time to catch a mouse and chase it
All around the house
But don't you
Lose it in the Lady's shoes...
Shoes, shoes, Lady's shoes...

Beatrice was amazed how much noise he could make with just one guitar and how fast the music took hold of her. Jake was right about one thing, Rufus knew how to dance. He took Beatrice and rocked her one way, then another, then twirled her round before picking her up and throwing her right through his lean, long legs. Beatrice gasped and giggled, then gasped again. She was too busy enjoying herself to take much notice of the party her markings were having. But just as the third song was coming to an end she realised, with some surprise, that her own gold bits had disappeared entirely. In their place was a pattern of black and white which looped and turned and stretched with the music while they danced.

"Psychedelic, man!" Jake nodded his approval from across the room where he was in the midst of a rather impressive guitar solo. "Real Sixties stuff. You sure you didn't eat any of them magic mushrooms while we were out, Bee?"

"You've stolen them," Beatrice turned to Rufus and shouted above the din. "I want them back. Give them back."

"My dear Princess, please don't upset yourself. It doesn't become you. I really don't understand what you are talking about." His voice was smooth, almost silky. "Exactly what am I supposed to have stolen?"

"My gold markings of course. Look at me. They're all gone."

Rufus put up an elegant paw and tweaked his whiskers. "I'm sorry my dear, you must be mistaken. There's no gold here. That would be for royalty, like yourself. I'm simply what you might call a Ginger Tom. Or a Ginger Rufus, I suppose. Why if I were gold they would have to call me Adonis."

He laughed in a self-deprecating way. Beatrice was about to tell him that she was nobody's dear, what was gold on one cat would be ginger on another and that breeding made all the difference, when he pulled her gently towards him and began to waltz and she completely forgot what she was going to say. She felt as though her insides were melting away and would soon be out of control just like her outsides.

"I beg you, my darling Princess, don't fret. What's mine is yours, of course and I hope what's yours is mine. But if you prefer to do a swap then just say the word."

Rufus's phrases sounded vaguely familiar but she couldn't remember where she had heard them before. "What's the word?" she asked.

"Why, you just said it! Your word, as they say, is my command."

The next second there was a strange whirring noise, like

the music had been played extra fast, and the whole room began to spin all over again. When it finally stopped turning Beatrice realised that now she was the one who was all gold. This time the dance partner in front of her was a strange black and white creature. He had a long pointy white nose and a black mask covering his eyes. His chest was white, and on his shoulders was what looked like a black cape. He had the longest legs Beatrice had ever seen – except his markings made him look like he was wearing the Lady's black stockings and suspenders.

"'Ello, my daarrleengs. Bravo Beatreeezia. Eesa true what they say about you. I haf waited and waited and I am not deesappointed."

Beatrice wanted to ask what they said about her, but she was rather worried what the answers might be. "And your name is?"

"Maverico, Marvellous Maverico, international rabbit runner and mouse maestro extraordinaire. Rico to my friends and admirers. 'Ere at your commando."

He tossed his masked head back, raised a front leg above his head and made a sort of snapping noise with his paw. Beatrice thought he didn't look like the sort of cat to take commands from anyone.

"I theenk ees time for some flamenco!"

Then he slapped both front paws together and started to strut about the place looking, Beatrice thought, completely ridiculous. But Jake's guitar music matched Maverico's movements – becoming strong, staccato, even arrogant. Beatrice, who now had music not just in her ears and her head but also in her heart and hips found herself moving along with it.

Maverico prowled around her, darting in and out with sharp movements. He pulled her this way and that, staring at her all the time through his mask. It was more like a battle than a dance. At one point, when she was off guard, he threw her to the floor, but she tripped him up (those long, gaitered legs were a liability) and stood over him with her golden paws on his white belly. For the first time in her life she actually felt like a queen. Jake's guitar playing came to a crescendo and then stopped.

"That's my girl Bee. But I think you need to let him go now." Jake's American accent suddenly sounded almost normal compared to this bizarre black and white creature.

Beatrice stepped away from her new partner somewhat reluctantly. He lay there for a few seconds then stretched out his long legs and flung himself into a backward somersault before bowing with a ridiculously huge flourish.

"But hey, what do I hear?" Jake's ears were pricked right up. "I think the Queen returns. Time for a change of mood. Rico, I need your help. You too Roof."

In all the excitement, Beatrice had quite forgotten about Rufus. But suddenly there he was, next to Jake, shimmering in the starlight and holding the old violin and a bow. Jake put his guitar on the floor and drew his long black tail across the strings. It produced a beautiful deep soft tone. The two of them began to play together. Maverico stood in front of them waving his long limbs around like a conductor. But the music they produced between them was gentle and surprisingly sweet.

"Ah, the ballet!" Sheba swept into the room, trailing little Candy in her wake. "So long since I was *en pointe*. Tell me boys, do you know Swan Lake?"

CHAPTER 8
A KITTEN-NAPPING

"Beatrice, put your markings back on properly this instant. Quite shameless!"

Beatrice opened her mouth to protest but, at a word from Sheba, the black and white markings reappeared and settled in between the gold ones in a rather pedestrian set of splodges. Beatrice felt the lightness within her disappear and a familiar heaviness take hold.

"Now girls, both of you, come over here to the barre. We must practise our pliés."

Queen Sheba was so excited by the prospect of playing the role of Odette that she seemed to have entirely forgotten her earlier humiliation at the hands of the Lady – not to mention her fright at the imaginary monster in the Wildwoods. Beatrice was quite relieved about this because she knew how angry and spiteful the Queen could get when she felt her dignity had been assaulted. Nevertheless she was cross at the way her mother had gate-crashed her private party.

"Since when did the banisters become a ballet barre?" she grumbled under her breath to Jake, who was busy retuning his guitar/violin and plucking the strings with his claws.

"Beatrice dear, do stop muttering. If you have something to say, say it loud and clear." The Queen paused for a second, fixing her daughter with a stare more reminiscent of a cobra about to strike than a lovelorn swan about to die. "No, I thought not. Now, stand up straight like Candy, toes turned out. That's better. And bend those knees…and straighten. Keep those spines straight."

Beatrice looked in front of her, where tiny Candy was bending and stretching, swaying and pointing, just as instructed. From the time they came into the room Candy had behaved almost as though Beatrice did not exist. She seemed to have eyes only for Queen Sheba. How could she have forgotten her real friend so easily?

After all, she thought bitterly, she was the one who had first discovered Candy. It had been Beatrice, not Sheba, who had taught her how to behave and had even set those exquisite markings in position so that she looked like a pedigree kitten and not some waif or stray. Why, Beatrice had even braved the Great Outdoors to search for her when she went missing. And this was the thanks she got. Beatrice was now the ugly, clumsy kitten, while Candy glowed and sparkled under Sheba's approving gaze, just as if she were the real Princess. How could Beatrice ever have considered such a goody-goody priss-pot a friend?

"Now I want you to see if you can both add a good swish of the tail as you come up. Like this."

Sheba's enormous tail swished so far that it ended up curled around Rufus's neck. He removed it carefully and returned it with a gallant bow. Beneath her muddled markings, Beatrice's skin crawled with resentment. What a creep Rufus was. To think she had been taken in by his looks and charm.

"Why thank you, kind sir. Perhaps we might try a pas-de-deux in a while. Or even an arabesque. I do like a strong partner." Sheba was positively simpering as she lifted her tail once more and ran it very deliberately down Rufus's spine. She turned back to her pupils.

"That's lovely, Candy. Of course, when it comes to tails you do have more material to work with, shall we say, than Beatrice. Look at that. Thick and white, just like a swan's wing. Lovely."

Sheba paused for a moment as if in ecstasy, but then her eyes flicked over to where her daughter stood, her multi-coloured markings a picture of disorder. Two black stripes hung diagonally above Beatrice's eyes, making her look even more cross than she felt, and her gold parts had sunk low beneath her belly.

"No, Beatrice, you are a graceful swan, not an angry alley-cat. Try to put some delicacy in your movements. And darling, do keep that thing under control. I think you have a lot more tail work to do. We will need daily practice from now on."

Beatrice didn't feel much like a swan either. Her tail had gone black and spiky and was spinning round and round furiously.

"Why, that tail looks more like the blades of a helicopter than a swan's feathers. Any moment now you will take off and fly right out of the window into the sky. What am I to do with her, boys?" Queen Sheba turned to the three musicians, shaking her head sadly and raising her eyes to heaven.

"Oh you don't want to go outside, Bee. Far too dangerous." Jake's deep voice held just a hint of mischief. It felt good to be sharing a secret with him.

"Why, I've heard there's an ogre passing through the Wildwoods tonight. Making the strangest noises. You think he's laughing, deep and loud and kinda mad, but next minute he done grab you and eat you right up. You two ladies never heard nothing like that while you were out tonight?"

"Y…Y…Yes," said Candy her white fur standing on end at the memory. But before she could elaborate, Sheba interjected.

"No, we heard nothing untoward at all. Maybe the odd owl hooting, but nothing to be alarmed about, did we my dear? After all, I am the Queen. Who would dare to harm me?" Her voice was light but her eyes were steel.

"Oh, no of course not. Silly me. Owls, of course. That's what is was." Candy looked down as she spoke. She could not meet that clear cold gaze. But neither could she look at Beatrice, who was trying to decide whether to be outraged or amused by her mother's lies.

"Well, that's good to know." Jake winked at Beatrice and addressed Sheba.

"Now, your Queenliness, if you want to try your paws at an arabesque, I recommend Rico here. Roof's OK at the modern stuff but well, Rico, he's classically trained – or so he says. Anyhow, looks like he's already wearing his ballet tights. Must make 'em in extra long sizes in Latin America, or wherever he's from."

Beatrice looked gratefully at Jake. The thought of Rufus doing a pas de deux with Sheba in front of her was just too much to bear. Maverico stretched one long, suspendered back leg up and over the top of his head before bringing it down and posing en pointe.

"My daarleeng Odette. Allow me to be your Siegfriedo. Already you haf captured my 'art." He executed a perfect pirouette without falling over and dropped to one knee before the Queen, where he stayed, his front legs raised in supplication.

"Ah well, in that case…." Sheba's voice trailed away and she looked into the distance. "I am in some ways a prisoner of my own beauty, you know. Perhaps you, my prince, will free me in the dance. But I wonder at what cost?" She left a dramatic pause and sighed soulfully.

Melodrama again, thought Beatrice disdainfully. How could they fall for it? Prisoner of her own beauty, my foot. Her own vanity perhaps. She should try being ugly for a while and see what that felt like. As if to underline the point, Beatrice's markings drew themselves into the ugliest scowls they could manage. Some of them even sketched lines on her sides, like prison bars. But no one was looking. All eyes were on the attic's principal dancers. There was a strange silence in the room – the sort of silence that is not empty but full – full of hope and expectation, but also fear and alienation. The silence that is the bridge between the past and the future but that is also the space between them.

The silence lasted maybe a few seconds if you looked at it one way on. If you looked at it another way it went on forever. Then Jake and Rufus picked up their instruments and began to play, but not the way they had played before. Earlier on it had been chords and solos, riffs and reels, with a bit of slapping and popping and a lot of showing off. Now music spilled from them the way the rain had spilled from the clouds, freely and abundantly, without effort. The melody was slow, haunting, heartbreaking and it came through the dancers just as it came through the musicians, as though they were all just instruments and the music was playing them all in different ways.

Sheba seemed to have got her wish and finally forgotten herself and her beauty in the dance. She bent and drooped, pointed and stretched, elevated and extended as though she were one with the music, not separate from it. Maverico's long limbs were now perfectly controlled, balancing and turning, lifting and leaping. Outside in the Wildwoods the wind sang mournfully and the trees were the corps de ballet, bending and bowing in unison. At the barre, Candy continued with her plies and port-de-bras in time with the music, though her eyes never left the dancers.

Only Beatrice stood apart, watching with a mixture of wonder and despair. She heard the music, felt the dance. She wanted to join in, to be a part of it all with the others and yet she couldn't move. Her limbs and her markings were frozen. It was as though they had got stuck in the earlier silence and she was nothing, nobody. Just the witness, a pair of lonely eyes and ears.

So only Beatrice noticed when the attic door began to move, very slowly. At first she thought it must be the wind, come to join the band. But the next moment there was a huge crash as the door opened fully and something burst into the space, snarling and spitting. The Thing raced around the room knocking over the Christmas decorations box and the piles of books, not to mention Jake, Rufus and Maverico, before dividing into two on either side of the room.

Sheba screeched loudly and, quite forgetting she was a lovelorn swan, ran to hide in the laundry basket, which would have amused Beatrice if she had not been so alarmed herself. Candy froze halfway through a *port de bras*. The boys simply looked dazed, as though someone had woken them up from a beautiful dream.

The first thing Beatrice noticed about the intruders was that they appeared to be cats, which was something of a relief. But they weren't the sort of cats she had become used to. One was black like Jake, except that, unlike Jake, he was thin – scrawny even. His right ear was torn and he had big yellow fangs which stuck out from his jaws menacingly. And he had only one eye. The other creature was black and white, like Maverico. But his white bits were filthy so you could hardly tell which parts were which. Like Maverico, he had a black mask, but it covered nearly all of his face so it looked like a balaclava with just the merest hint of a dirty white chin poking out below. He, too, was painfully thin. Inside the mask his eyes flashed black and gold. Amber and onyx, thought Beatrice, recalling Sheba's lessons in precious stones.

"Well, fancy that, Flakey-Jakey." The scruffy black cat spoke through his fangs, his mouth hardly moving. "You're having a party and you didn't invite us." He stalked around the attic, his head low like a panther.

"Have to say it looks like you ain't having such a wild time without us though. Never thought I would see the day Flakey-Jakey went to the ballet." He kicked a pile of boxes over.

"But then I wouldn't have thought you'd be hobnobbing with Royalty either. Or should I say ex-Royalty? A sad old has-been Queen and her freak of a handmaid."

His single eye swept over Beatrice whose markings had now come unstuck and were doing a good impression of a pogo dance.

"Don't you call her a freak." Jake was back on his feet now. His back arched and his tail stood upright. It was so huge that it was almost brushing the sloping attic ceiling. "She's worth a dozen of you Gangsta and well more than a dozen once she learns control of herself."

He stopped suddenly as though he had said something wrong. The next moment he took an enormous leap and landed right on top of the skinny intruder. The two of them rolled around on the floor with lots of snarling, yelling, biting and scratching. Jake had weight on his side, but Gangsta was clearly the fighting sort. From somewhere inside the laundry basket came Sheba's voice.

"What did I say about the Wild West? I told you not to go mixing with his type. Now here we are with a full-scale bar-room brawl. Look at what you have done, Beatrice."

Beatrice was about to reply that her mother hadn't complained about the ballet music when there was a loud crash and Gangsta's head popped up from inside the body of Rufus's guitar. The rest of the instrument was wrapped around his neck. His single eye was glazed over and his whiskers were tangled in the strings.

"I do apologise, Your Majesty, and to you young ladies, but drastic times call for drastic action." Rufus's smooth mellow tones sounded very strange after all the din. "I don't think he'll be going anywhere in a hurry."

Maverico, who had been remarkably quiet till then, picked up the violin bow. "Normally I play weeth – 'ow you say 'ere – the cat guts? But you know the wheeskers might work just as well."

He started drawing the bow back and fore across Gangsta's

trapped whiskers. It made a strange whining noise, but not as strange as the noise which came from Gangsta's throat, which was made up of howls of pain mixed up with growls of fury.

"Ees good, no?" Maverico was clearly enjoying himself. "Bad, yes. Gangsta ees very bad cat. But ees still good to make beautiful music together my friend, yes?"

The bad cat Gangsta snarled, and then he smiled – as far as that was possible with his whiskers trapped in the guitar strings. His yellow fangs appeared to be the only teeth he had left.

"Well, I guess you think you've done well here. But you really ain't got no idea. Ain't you missing something? While you've been busy making music with me you ain't even noticed that your pretty princess is a-gonna.

"Old Grubsta, he mayn't look too bright but he's the silent type you know. So much for the Knights Protector eh? Well, we've got your bonny princess now. Which means we'll rule the Wildwoods too. At least we will when this old crone croaks." Gangsta looked across at Sheba with disdain. "Which will be soon, I promise."

Maverico dropped his bow in astonishment. Seizing his chance, Gangsta twisted his head sharply and released his whiskers and then smashed himself into the wall so that the guitar broke into pieces and he was free.

"You don't know what you are talking about. I'm still here," Beatrice piped up, but Jake stopped her talking by wrapping his front paws round her mouth.

"Very silly of us, I'm sure." Rufus's silky tones had a slightly rough edge for once. "You are right, we should have been paying attention. But I assure you, wherever she is, wherever you try to hide her we will find her. And we will bring her home."

Gangsta laughed – a cruel, triumphant laugh – as he slunk out of the attic door. Was he winking as he left? Or was it just his single eye blinking?

Only then, with Jake's paws still holding her tight, did Beatrice realise the truth. Candy was missing. They had mistaken Candy for the Princess and kidnapped her.

CHAPTER 9

A COLOURFUL PAST

The cats looked at each other in silence – the sort of silence that gapes like the mouth of a cave, so dark and huge and mysterious that you dare not enter. Then suddenly everyone spoke at once.

"I told you, Beatrice," said Queen Sheba.

"I say, that's a bit rum. Took our eye off the ball there good and proper. Have to get our thinking caps on," said Rufus.

"Ees a keed-napping, a keeten-napping. We must declare zee war prontissimo," said Maverico.

"It's all my fault. I hated her, and now she's gone." said Beatrice.

Jake waited until they had all finished. "Well now, that was a near miss," he said.

"A near miss? When dear little Candy's missing? Why she might even be…" Sheba stopped herself before the word came out. "How can you be so heartless?"

"Well now you of all people should understand that, Queenie," Jake said, pointedly. Sheba looked at him for a moment with fury, then dropped her eyes and fell deep into her own silence. He turned to the group.

"Point is, he didn't get the real Princess. She's safe with us. And that's the main thing."

Beatrice felt like saying that she didn't feel safe at all, given that two filthy, dirty old criminals had just managed to walk in from the woods, kidnap Candy and leave with only the odd damaged whisker. But she didn't want to seem ungrateful to Jake, whose loyalty was touching.

"See, Bee," he continued, "sooner or later they gonna realise they got the wrong kitten, and then they gonna let her go. Or else…"

"Or else what?" Beatrice's voice was shaking and so were her markings.

"Or else, we're going to have to find her and bring her back to us, of course." But for once, he didn't sound too sure of himself.

Beatrice was just about to ask Jake how he intended to make this happen when Maverico leapt into the centre of the room. He had found some broken beanpoles in a cupboard and was brandishing one of them like a sword.

"Where ees he? Zees coward cat zey call zee Grubsta? I weel find him and challenge heem to a jewel. Not for nothing was I brought up in ze 'ouse of Zorro. I 'ave zee Certificate in Swordsmanship, Level Two with Deesteenction. So I know 'ow to buckle ze squash with ze best of zem. Ees Magnifico Maverico, no?"

He swung the beanpole from side to side fiercely before poking it hard into Jake's belly. The stress of the morning proved too much for the normally peaceable Jake. He snatched the beanpole and broke it over Maverico's head.

"I say, old chaps," Rufus stepped in between them, "calm down. Been a bit of a tough morning. But we can't just go racing around the woods like demented rabbits. I think this calls for a spot of strategy, don't you?

"Now I don't want to blow my own trumpet," Rufus coughed in a self-deprecating fashion, "but I have done some officer training myself before I was recruited into the Service. And I would be more than happy to share my expertise."

Beatrice interrupted. "I should go and look for her. It's my fault she's gone. I was the one who encouraged her to visit.

65

And then I was thinking all these horrid thoughts about her. And it's because of me that she's been taken." She paused to get her breath back. All the emotion had quite taken it out of her. "Though I still don't know why they wanted me and not you, Mummy. After all you are the Queen."

There was another silence. This time it was a silence full of secrets – like when you watch someone through a sound-proof window and you can't tell whether they are singing or screaming. Maverico and Rufus started to cough uncontrollably. Even Jake turned his face away.

Eventually, Sheba spoke. "All I can say, darling, is there's no accounting for commoners. In any case, after that excitement I have quite a headache. I need to rest. But when I come back I expect you three boys to have come up with some sort of plan.

"As for you Beatrice," she looked her daughter up and down, "I really don't think there is much point in you Contemplating Beauty today. But you can get on with your tail work." And with that she swept from the room.

Beatrice regarded her tail, which had quite a fetching pattern of ginger and white rings. It twitched back at her furiously.

"Don't you take that tone with me," she began. But then she stopped. Suddenly she felt so tired that she could no longer stand up. It had been a long night, what with the Great Outdoors and the party and the gangsters and the kitten-napping.

"There, there, do try to calm down. It's not the end of the world," she told her tail, in what she hoped was a comforting tone.

It must have worked, because as she settled down next to the banisters, her tail curled itself around her belly in an affectionate, well-behaved sort of way, though the rings refused to budge. Then Jake cuddled down on the other side of her. Across the room Maverico and Rufus were deep in discussions about military strategy. All she could hear was the odd word. "Commandant…storm the camp…camouflage." None of it made sense.

"Jake?"

Jake put a big paw on her shoulder. "What's up Little Bee? Not feeling Bee-Littled I hope by old Queenie and her nonsense." He chortled with pleasure at his own wit, almost as if everything was back to normal.

"Jake, how can you laugh when Candy could be, well, she could be dead?"

"Know something, Lil' Bee, I don't think they'll hurt her just yet. And when they realise they've made a mistake, they're gonna want to do some bargaining. I reckon that's when you might get to show your true colours, Lil' Bee."

Beatrice had no idea what he was talking about but she felt too tired to ask him to explain. Still, there was one thing she needed to know.

"Jake?"

"Yes, Your Beeity?"

"What did they mean when they said my mother is a has-been Queen?"

There was a pause before Jake replied. He sighed heavily.

"Why I guess you need to know the story some time. Just didn't expect it to be so soon. You just close your eyes and I'll tell you it like a bedtime story. And if you go to sleep, why, it don't matter. We can do the rest another day. You ready?"

Beatrice nodded and Jake began.

"Once upon a time, long before you were born, your father lived here. His name was Leon, and he was the King of the Furthest Kingdom which, as you know, includes the Wildwoods. King Leon was strong and powerful and handsome, of course, but he was also noble and kind, and under his rule the woods prospered. The trees grew extra tall and the badgers built their underground city and the birds sang all year round, even in the darkest winters. By day the bees and the butterflies tended to the flowers in the gardens and at night the bats swooped in and out of the treetops and generally kept an eye on things. Folks say they're blind but they sort of see with their ears, if you understand me."

Beatrice did not understand but she wanted to hear the rest of the story so she said nothing.

"Anyhow, one night the bats reported an abandoned cat crawling across the fields on the edge of the woods. King Leon went to investigate. He found this creature, so filthy you couldn't tell what colour she was. She was full of ticks and fleas and so starving and thin you'd swear you could almost see right through her.

"Well, King Leon couldn't leave her there, so he rescued her and brought her back to his cave in the woods. She told him some story 'bout how she'd been brought over from Egypt by a bunch of criminals. Trafficked, she called it. Said she'd escaped by hiding in a car but then the people drove off and she jumped out and found herself in the middle of nowhere. Well, obviously it wasn't the middle of nowhere, it was actually the edge of somewhere, but she didn't know it at the time."

"How dreadful," Beatrice gasped, opening her eyes wide, even though the lids were as heavy as tree trunks. "Poor thing. Whatever happened to her?"

"Oh you don't need to worry about that Bee. King Leon cleaned her up himself and fed her the finest rabbits and pigeons and soon old Sheba put some weight on. For that of course is who the stranger was. And once she began to feel better and to look better, well, she began to enjoy the attention. King Leon became besotted with her. Why, he even went off and brought her some fresh trout from the stream cos she said the rabbit was too tough or something like that. In the beginning, he took her hunting with him and tried to teach her to fend for herself but she was having none of it. Put on these airs and graces, just like she piled on the weight.

"She became beautiful – at least on the outside – but us courtiers didn't like her. She bossed us around all the time. Nothing was ever right for her. Anyhow, the King couldn't see it. He was in love with her and, well, one thing led to another and she became Queen Sheba. Then of course, there was no stopping her. She wanted crystals and tapestries to line the cave and Leon, he went out searching, but all he could find was some old fossils and a bale of hay, which didn't go down too well, I can tell you."

"I can imagine," said Beatrice, smiling to herself. The rest of the story had been so shocking that Beatrice's markings had tried to do somersaults, but they were too tired so they had given up and now, at last, they seemed to have settled down for the night.

"Old Leon, he took to disappearing for longer and longer periods lookin' for those crystals. We never knew quite where he was but he always came back.

"Anyhow, next thing is, she's expecting you, of course, and she develops these cravings. Double cream. She just has to have it. Well old Leon, he's lived all his life in the woods. He don't even know what cream is, let alone where to find it. But she won't let up. Wailing and whingeing every night till one day the King decides he needs to go into the city himself to look for it.

"He set off one night on his own, wouldn't let no one come with him. It was a snowy winter's night and he just headed off up that path…" Jake stopped. His voice had grown thick.

"And, well, we never saw him again. We went out in groups, looking. We sent messages via the foxes and the red kites – they are all moving into the cities you know, so we asked them to keep a look-out. But we never heard nothin' back, to this day.

"We don't know whether he got hit by a car and crawled away somewhere. Or whether he found a new kingdom – one of those new housing estates they keep building. Maybe he's just off a-huntin' crystals some place. Or maybe he just liked the double cream too much and decided to stay. But, you know, Old Leon, he'd never have left his Kingdom, or his Queen for that matter, without good reason – especially not with you on the way."

"What did Mother do?"

"Well, Sheba, she went quiet for a while. Then she went funny. That's when she started making up more stories, like the ones you've heard about Egypt and pyramids and being a goddess and so on. She done forgot about the Kingdom – or the Queendom, as it had become.

"And so everything went a bit wild – even for the Wildwoods. No one knowed who was in charge, really. And actually there weren't no one in charge. There were gangs roamin' the woods – cats from the cities, from other villages, even from other woods. They didn't know how to treat our woods. They were rude to the badgers. They desecrated the fairy sites. They ran riot with the rabbits. Old Leon had instituted a rabbit quota system so the rabbits got a fair chance and we all got a continuous supply. It worked well as long as no one got greedy.

"But this lot, they just killed everything they saw, just for the hell of it. Thrushes, blackbirds, robins. Soon there were no birds left to sing in the woods and no mice to play with. It became such a sad, place, like a forgotten world. Even the trees started to die just from broken hearts, like. And then in the middle of it all, you came along." Suddenly Jake guffawed with laughter. "That was the best laugh we'd had in months."

"Why, what was wrong with me?" Beatrice felt her heart sink.

"Nothing was wrong, Sweet Bee. Nothing at all. Just you wasn't the kitten the Queen was expecting. She thought she'd get a purrfect mini-me – all cute and white and fluffy. And when she saw you she went nuts. Said you were a mistake. Shouted and bawled. Said someone must have swapped you when she wasn't looking. Why, she was all for taking you off into the city and just leaving you. That's when some of us got together and approached the High Lord."

"Oh dear. Was I so ugly? Oh, I knew I was a mistake, I wish I had never been born." Beatrice's voice trembled and she hid her face underneath her paws. Jake curled his front legs tightly around her.

"Ugly? Why no Bee. Not at all. That weren't the problem. The problem was that you were magnificent."

Beatrice peeped out from between her paws. "Don't be silly, Jake. You don't have to be nice to me. All these colours and patches and spots and stripes and stuff. That Gangsta was right. I'm a freak."

"Let me tell you, young lady, those colours are just the beginning. Why, when you were born you weren't just white and gold and black. You were all the colours of the rainbow – plus a few more that I guess haven't been invented yet. Why you were so bright and sparkling it was hard for the rest of us to look at you. Bit of a shock for everyone, but for old Sheba – well, it was like a smack in the teeth. She thought she was the Beautiful One. And then you came along."

"It's a nice thought Jake, but it doesn't make sense. Why I've only got three colours now and I can't even manage those. I couldn't dazzle anybody. If it's true, like you say, what happened to the other colours?"

"Well, when Old Sheba kicked off like that, the Elders of the Wildwoods – the badgers and the foxes and the crows and the squirrels and the owls, mainly – they were so concerned that they went to the High Lord of the Dale and asked for help."

"Who's the High Lord?"

"The High Lord is more than a king and less than a god. And he oversees not just the Wildwoods but all the hills and dales for miles around. He can take lots of forms but that day he came to us as a stag. Oh Bee, you should have seen him. His antlers were real trees growing out the top of his head, with branches and leaves and everything. Even has birds singing in there some days, they say. His name is Francis, but he prefers us to call him Frank.

"So he called Sheba in and you were there too, but you were only tiny and your eyes hadn't opened yet. High Lord Frank told her there and then that she was a disgrace to the Queendom and the Wildwoods and to motherhood. And he banished her, just like that, on the spot. She was sent to live with the Lady, the one you have now, on the edge of the woodland, sort of in exile. And she has no power, not any more. And the Wildwoods? Well, guess they've just gone wild for the time being. Ain't no one in charge really.

"Thing is, then there was the question of what to do with you. You'd done nothing wrong, you didn't deserve punishment. And you certainly needed protection. But Sheba she suddenly changed her mind about you, went all sloppy, and started talking about the importance of a mother's milk and how you were all she'd got left and all that sort of stuff.

"So High Lord Frank decided that she could take you with her until you are old enough and wise enough to inherit the Queendom. But in order to protect you from the Queen's jealousy and from those who might recognise you and want to harm you, he used his magic powers to make some of your colours disappear.

"He was going to put the missing colours in a big chest and bury it in the woods, but then he had a better idea. He decided to scatter them about and hide them inside other colours, where no one would ever think of looking. So he put some up inside the blue sky and others in the green leaves and the golden sun and then some of the brightest, most unusual colours he hid them inside the birds and flowers."

"But that's stealing!" said Beatrice indignantly.

"Oh, he ain't taken them away for good, you understand. They're just sort of held in trust for you till you're ready for 'em. Ready to be a proper Queen. He just left you the three colours to be going on with – and as you know, he sort of mixed those up a bit. So you have something to practise on, I guess."

"I so want to be beautiful," Beatrice sighed.

"Thing is, Bee, with beauty like that you have to be careful. It's powerful stuff. Those colours, they can brighten someone's day or they can blind someone. You need to learn how to use them properly."

"What d'you mean?"

"Well, just say some real ugly ol' cat comes to you for help."

"Like Gangsta?"

"Yes, I guess, like Gangsta. Well, you shining like a cut diamond, that ain't necessarily goin' to help him. Could just make him feel worse 'bout himself. So when you're ready, you'll know how to sort of adjust your colour and brightness a little, just so's he don't feel overwhelmed and then take it from there. It's not just about being right, it's about being kind too. But all that's a long way off and quite a complicated operation of course. First things first. You need to keep the ones you've got from racing about all over the place when they like."

"I suppose so." Beatrice sighed again. "There's such a lot to learn. But what if the sky and the trees and all the others won't give me my colours back?"

Jake smiled. "Those colours always be there Bee. They're just hidin'. Why, I like to think that every time you see a flower, or look up into the sky, or watch the jays and the goldfinches you can think, 'Why that's a piece of me – right there'. Just remember, no one can't take nothin' from you that's yours. Anyhow, you need to get some shut-eye, cos tomorrow we need to go find little Candy and bring her home."

CHAPTER 10
TALL TAILS

"I don't think I want to be magnificent," said Beatrice.

It was evening once again. Rufus and Maverico had spent the night and the best part of the day devising their strategy while Jake and Beatrice slept. Now the four cats were gathered outside on the patio. Sheba was lying down inside, pleading a headache.

"Pain in the neck, more like," muttered Jake. "Anyway, Baybee, what's wrong with being magnificent?"

"Ssshhh," said Rufus. "We are on reconnaissance now. I need silence and discipline."

"It's too big," said Beatrice.

"Hard to find a Mini-nificence, I'd say," Jake said, ignoring Rufus's stern expression.

"Never worry, Piccolissima. Magnifico ees good." Maverico's voice rang out across the garden and shook the branches of the trees. "I know of course. I am after all the Magnificent Maverico."

Jake was becoming just the teeniest bit irritated. "More like Awesome Jawsome if you ask me. Roof's right, we need to keep the noise down. Carry on like that and the whole wood's gonna know what we're up to. And we're gonna be a gonna."

Despite the seriousness of the occasion, Beatrice smiled. Rufus, however, was not amused. "I say chaps, this won't do. If I'm to lead this operation I need to know you're on my side.

And that means listening to what I say and doing what I tell you. Is that agreed?" The three cats nodded silently. "Now, if I could have your attention?"

Maverico stood up on his long legs and began a military salute.

"Not that sort of attention, Rico," Rufus said tetchily. "Just listen, OK?"

"The first thing we have to do is find out where the Bad Cats have taken Candy. It's been a good few hours now and they have had time to move her around a bit. I'm guessing they are working for The General, but we don't even know where The General hangs out these days. She'll be in a prison cell somewhere. We just have to find out where."

"Wow, I can see why they spent so long devising a strategy last night," Jake muttered sarcastically.

"Who's The General?" Beatrice tried to whisper but it came out as more of a chirrup. Rufus glared at her.

"Tell you later," Jake winked. "But for now all you need to know is he's one Bad Cat."

"To continue," said Rufus, testily, "I've been briefing the bats, at least those squadrons who remain loyal to the Kingdom – or should I say Queendom." He bowed slightly towards Beatrice, who felt her marking melting like hot jelly under his clear emerald gaze. "Anyhow they are out all over the woods on reconnaissance as we speak."

"How will they know where to find us?" asked Beatrice.

"Ah-ha, good question. I have my special sonic echo-lo-cator whistle." Rufus produced something from his leather collar and blew on it triumphantly. There was a long pause.

"I don't hear nothing," Jake said. Maverico was busy making wild silent gestures with his ears.

Rufus was unfazed. "That's because only bats can hear it."

"Gee, that's useful. So how they gonna know it's you speaking and not a bat."

"Ah, that's the clever thing. There's a special identifying click built into the call. State of the art batphone, I suppose you'd call it. Of course the owls will be on the look-out too, but they are, by nature, more conspicuous."

"But how are we going to hear what the bats are saying to us?" asked Beatrice.

"Good point again, your Royal Highness," Rufus nodded approvingly. "I've devised a code – a sort of sign language. It will all become clear, you'll see."

"Which is more than those bats will," Jake muttered.

"And when we 'ave found these maleficent moggees, then we keel them, no?" Maverico was practising his martial arts moves.

"Well, we'll have to tread carefully. The aim, as always, is to retrieve the captive with the least loss of life. But The General's headquarters is a network of caves, according to the bats. And we will have to get past his guards. It's a bit of a labyrinth, I understand."

"Enough of your conversazione." Maverico had now moved on to the full fitness routine and was in the middle of a series of press-ups. He leapt to his feet. "We need to be, 'ow you say, up and hat'm!"

Jake looked round. "Yeah, guess we really should be making a move. But does your strategy give us actually any indication of which direction we need to take?"

"Indeed it does," said Rufus, ignoring Jake's cynicism. "The first thing we need to do is to shut our eyes."

"Sounds like a plan," said Jake, giving a big stretch and yawning ostentatiously.

"Stop it Jake," said Beatrice. "This is serious."

They closed their eyes as instructed.

"Now, I want you all to imagine Candy. Bring her to mind exactly as you last saw her. Such a tiny kitten. Think very hard." Rufus's voice had taken on a sing-song quality.

Maverico, Jake and Beatrice, eyes tight shut, were swaying slightly in time with his words.

"Picture her in her chains. Allow your mind to wander through the woods. Allow it to take you to her. See Candy in all her beauty. And her captivity. See her where she is now. And know that when you open your eyes your path will be before you. Simple really. Now on my count, one, two three, *OPEN.* Everyone ready? And, off we go."

Jake, Rufus, Maverico and Beatrice did as they were told and strode off confidently. The only problem was they each chose a different direction. Jake went east, Rufus went north, Maverico went south and Beatrice went west, which took her straight back into the patio doors where she bumped her head badly.

"Whoah, whoah! Halt! Halt, I said." Rufus shouted after Maverico who was disappearing out of sight. He scratched his head with his back leg. "That's not how it's meant to work."

They thought for a while.

"Perhaps if we linked tails and did it?" Beatrice wondered.

"Nice idea, Bee," Jake agreed. "You're not as daft as you're kitten-looking."

"I suppose we could try that," Rufus said, a bit grudgingly, "though it didn't say anything about that in the Remote Viewing section of the Espionage Training Manual."

And so the four of them stood close together, facing away from each other, each with their tails held high.

"Guess I'll go first," said Jake, and he wound his large, fat, black tail around Rufus's muscular, sinewy one. "Have to say, though, this all feels a lil' intimate for my taste."

"Ecco, ecco' ere' comes, il grande!" Maverico unfurled his black and white tail with a huge flourish, like a magician pulling a rabbit out of a hat. The tail waved and pointed and curled and uncurled itself dramatically.

"Oh do get on with it Rico!" Rufus was getting impatient. "You are holding up the entire operation."

"By all means, messieurs, dames." Rico allowed his tail to circle round Jake's and Rufus's.

"And now you, MagnifiBee."

"Do stop it Jake. I'm only little. How am I going to get my tail right up there?"

Jake thought for a moment. "Know something, kid? You don't have to reach so hard. Why, you just need to stretch a little and then let your markings do it for you."

Beatrice looked puzzled, then she stretched her tail up as far as it would go. "Like this? Now what?"

"That's it, Bee. Stretch – and let them go. Think like you're firing arrows from a bow. Deep breath in – and on the out-breath – fire!"

Beatrice wasn't sure what a bow or an arrow was, but she liked the idea of letting go. Her markings shot right up the tail tower, like a flag up a flagpole.

As always they were a bit undisciplined. On their way up they hit Maverico in the eyes, giving him a large ginger patch. Rufus also ended up with a black nose, but not for long. In seconds nearly all of her markings had reached the top and there were only enough left to cover Beatrice very thinly. Then, apparently of their own accord, they began to weave themselves in and out of the other tails. In and out they went, up and down, until they had made a single large, multi-coloured plait.

"That's Royalty for you. Brings the people together like nothing else," said Jake.

"Hush!" Rufus reassumed command. "Thank you, your Royal Highness," and he tried to bow again. But he had reckoned without the tail tower which pulled all the others on top of him as he bent over. He managed to straighten up just before the entire thing collapsed.

"So altogether now," he ordered. *"One Four All and All Four One."*

"*One Four All and All Four One,*" the cats chorused dutifully.

"That's good. So, eyes closed again. And, *All, Four, One*, think Candy."

There was a strange sort of rumble, like the deepest purr imaginable, and then silence. A wide, welcoming silence, like the inside of a circle. It was so nice they stayed that way for a while with their eyes closed, and their tails bound together, aloft.

"Now, open!" said Rufus. They opened their eyes, a little dazed.

"And, on my count – *All, Four, One* – unwind!" The tails undid themselves easily, like a spring uncoiling. Beatrice's markings plaited themselves neatly around her tummy and thighs.

"And – Turn!" The four cats turned to face each other.

"Well?" said Beatrice.

"Well, well," said Jake.

"Well, I never," said Rufus. "It's worked."

Coming from the point between them was a path they had never seen before. It was muddy, like all the Wildwoods paths, but its sides were lined with tiny quartz crystals which sparkled and twinkled in the moonlight, stretching away deep into the woods.

"What do you know? Ees just lika ze cats' eyes, no?" Maverico marvelled – and for once not at himself.

"Come along then," Rufus was confident once more. "On the double, there's no time to lose."

The cats set off confidently but as soon as their paws touched the path it began to wriggle beneath them like a live creature. Beatrice kept falling over and then apologising for hurting it – just in case it really was alive. The path did not reply – but neither did it keep still.

The cats tried lying down, but they rolled off. They tried crouching and pouncing on it, but it escaped each time and leapt further away. In the end they found the best thing to do was to jump on it and then run as fast as they could so their feet were on the ground as little as possible. That way they hoped they could trick the path into thinking they were not actually there at all.

Still the path was not an easy one. It went up and down and round and round and in and out and even upside down.

"Reminds me of my days as a Spitfire pilot," gasped Rufus as the path righted itself abruptly.

"Reminds me of those rides at Disneyland," said Jake, picking himself up off the ground for the umpteenth time.

"What's Disneyland?" asked Beatrice.

"It's like a pretend Wildwoods back home, invented by humans," said Jake. "There's fairies and princesses and film characters and rollercoaster rides and stuff. Thing is, it's not like the Wildwoods because it ain't real and it ain't dangerous."

Just as he spoke the path dropped away, as though it were falling over the side of an invisible cliff. The four cats dropped with it, turning somersaults as they went. The air rushed past their ears and then right through them till the inside of their heads felt empty like the sky. Their tails fanned out behind them like parachutes and their whiskers blew backwards and forwards like wings. They fell through the air for miles, tossing and turning till they were unaware of where they were and even who they were. Sometimes they caught a glimpse of fur falling – but none of them could have been sure just whose fur it was. And then, just when they had given themselves up entirely, when they had ceased to worry about falling, or even landing, everything suddenly stopped. They found themselves upright, as cats do after a fall. The moss was soft beneath their paws but the path itself had disappeared and around them the woods were eerily still.

"See what I mean?" said Jake, shaking himself. "This ain't no game. This here's the real deal."

Beatrice's markings, which had scattered like dust as she fell, now settled back on top of her in particles so fine she looked misty, like an impressionist painting.

"Ees an outrage!" Maverico was untangling his long limbs and inspecting them for damage. "These legs, they are dancer's legs. They are not to be lightly crossed."

Rufus was on the batphone. "Cat Courtier to Bat Battalion, come in please!" He blew hard on his silent whistle. The three others looked around them.

"Ain't never seen this part of the Wildwoods before," said Jake.

They stood on top of a hill, which was strange in itself, given that they had fallen such a long way down to get there. Before them was a large flat slab of white rock. All around the rock were huge trees with long dangly branches.

"Ees not a wood. Ees a jungle. Zees tree, though, I see them somewhere before. Zey are ze ones which puzzle ze monkeys, no?" Just then one of the monkey trees put out a long root and tripped him up so that he landed face down in the mud. Another one wrapped its long branches around Jake's neck, like a scarf.

"Quite fetching, doncha think, Bee?" he asked, rubbing his neck luxuriously against the spiky leaves. "And almost as satisfyin' as a good scratch."

"Cat Courtier to Bat Battalion, come in please." Rufus was still on the batphone. "Could you advise on coordinates please? It is now a matter of urgency!"

"Well, it's not like you are going to hear them reply is it?" said Jake, then ducked fast as a bat came whizzing past his shoulder, missing him by a whisker.

Suddenly the woods were alive with bats, swooping and circling in the moonlight, dipping and diving from the tree-tops, before zooming over the cats' heads and back up into the dark sky.

"Guess that's what they call air-robics – or maybe it should be acro-bat-ics," Jake chuckled. "What do you think, Rico?" But Maverico's head was buried in Beatrice's belly.

"I 'ate these bats. Ees a phobia. From ze days I fought with Zorro in Transylvania. Away, away, you vampires!" He waved his tail around frantically.

"I say, old boy, no need to be so wet," said Rufus. "These aren't vampire bats, they're pipistrelles. Soprano pipistrelles actually. I thought with your operatic knowledge you would appreciate that. They're tiny things these, just like little flying mice."

"Oh yeah?" Jake was suddenly interested.

"No, no, these are our friends, Jake." Beatrice looked up from comforting Maverico. "We can't hurt them. They are going to tell us where Candy is."

"Really?" Jake dodged another low flyer. "Don't know how, since they are blind and we can't hear a darn thing they say."

"Ingenious, absolutely ingenious." Rufus was staring at the pale rock in front of them, beneath which the bats had been doing their acrobatics.

Jake followed his gaze. "Jeepers, creepers, I can't believe my peepers. Is that a map they've drawn? But how have they…? How did they…?" For once even Jake was lost for words.

"Rico, it's alright, they've gone." Beatrice felt quite grown up as she stroked his trembling shoulders. "And just look at what they have left behind." Maverico slowly withdrew his head and looked at the pattern covering the white stone.

"Quite simple really." Rufus could not keep a touch of smugness out of his voice. "Guano, that's what it's drawn with. The bats just made sure to eat a few extra dodgy midges – the ones that hang around the cow pats. And Bob's your uncle – or I should say the bats are your mapmakers. Just requires a bit of control as they, well, you know. Otherwise all the boundaries would be, well, a bit blurred.

"But here we have it. A perfect map, showing us exactly where Candy is being held. At least that's what it's meant to be." He was staring hard at the map in front of him, with a slightly puzzled expression.

"Old Jake, he might call zis a Batticelli, no?" Maverico, now recovered, stamped his paws and waved his arms in the air, like the hero he claimed to be. "Olé!"

"Nice one Rico," said Jake. "But less of the old. Now let's take a good look and see where we go next. It don't look that simple to me."

* * *

"I jus' don't get it," Jake scratched his ear in puzzlement.

The cats were sitting in different places around the great flat rock, so that together they formed the four corners of a square. Rufus had decided this was the best way to examine the map left by the bats.

"Got to make sure we cover all the angles," he decreed.

"Trouble is," said Jake, "there ain't no angles. This here map's a circle. Or maybe more of a spiral, actually." He cocked his head to one side for a better look. "Those guano lines jus' go round and round but maybe they're supposed to take us to the middle."

"You're right, Jake," said Rufus. "We just have to find where to start from."

"Here!" shouted Beatrice. "It's by this big stone. There's a gap, look." So the four cats gathered by the stone and set off in single file along the guano pathway following the spiral towards the centre of the circle. Rufus led the way and Jake brought up the rear. Round and round they went. And round and round and round again till they were so dizzy they couldn't see the guano lines and the wood span around them as they walked.

"My 'ead, eet ees spinning, with all this spiralising," Maverico complained.

84

"Bloomin' batty I say," said Jake stopping to scratch his head with his back leg. The effort proved too much and he fell over.

"That's weird," said Beatrice. "I thought we were right near the middle but now we seem to be going back out again."

It was true. The map was leading them right back the way they had come. The return journey, if that is what it was, took even longer than the outward trip and at the end of all their walking they found themselves back where they had begun, at the entrance to the spiral, next to the big grey stone, dizzy and even more confused.

"Bit of a rum do," said Rufus. "Don't know what those bats were playing at."

"Dunno," said Jake, rubbing his eyes. "Maybe I'm not seeing straight after all that circle dancing, but don't this stone look different to you?"

The cats regarded it silently. Jake was right. The ordinary grey rock they had set off from seemed much bigger than before and it was also a different shape. It now looked more like huge stone pillar set on its side – or perhaps an old fallen tree trunk. And at one end of it there was a big hole, the sort that Jake had told Beatrice usually marked an entrance to Badger City.

"That's it!" Rufus muttered. "Can't think how we missed it first time round." But he looked worried, rather than relieved.

"Why, what is it?" asked Beatrice, excitedly.

Rufus harrumphed and paused before speaking. "That, my friends," he said gravely, "is the fossilised tree."

"So, 'e is just an old fossil – nothing to worry about," said Maverico. "But what is zis 'ole? A secret passagero, no? Ees narrow? I can do ze belly dance, to go where no cat has gone before. I am belly-dance champion in Brazil."

To prove the point he put his belly flat to the floor, stretched his long legs out front and back and began to arch and straighten his back repeatedly, pushing himself along the ground as he did so.

"Actually, this is serious." Rufus's green eyes were troubled. "The fossilised tree is hundreds of millions of years old. Look carefully and you'll see the stone is patterned and ridged just like tree bark.

"And that hole there isn't just any old badger run. It's actually a hole in Time. Go down there and heaven only knows what's before us – or behind us for that matter. That's if we can get past the tree in the first place. The tree's job is to guard this entrance."

"I don't understand," said Beatrice. "If that's where Candy is then…"

Rufus's expression was grim. "Then she could be lost in Time."

Beatrice had no idea what Time was, really, but she knew from the way Rufus pronounced it that this Time would begin with a capital letter, like Queen or Princess. She knew when it was time to eat or sleep or play or study Catiquette. But she did not understand how Time could be a place where you got lost. Looking at Rufus's face, though, she knew better than to ask him.

"Don't look like much of a guard, either way. Can't move for a start," said Jake, dismissively.

"Don't be so sure," said Rufus. "This is one fearsome fossil. You see those long thin bits of stone lying around next to it?" The cats leaned over to look. "They're the tree branches, or they were 350 million years ago and they've got some life in them, I can tell you. We need to watch out. But we have to get past them if we are to rescue Candy."

"Don't sound like we have much choice then," said Jake.

A few yards away Maverico was doing a series of yoga stretches. "See 'ow I shifta my shape. Ees like magic. See 'ere, I am ze cat," he arched his back and then curved it the other way. "And ze next I am ze downward dog." He stretched his back legs up as far as they would go and crouched down at the front. Beatrice tried to copy him but her markings kept sliding down onto her nose so she couldn't see.

"This is no time for messing about," said Rufus. "We must show respect. The Time Tunnel can be a deadly place for those who seek only self-aggrandisement. Even for those with nobler purpose it may prove a Time of Trial. Are we all prepared?"

He looked round at his friends. Maverico had stopped cavorting. Jake was sitting up, looking uncharacteristically serious, and Beatrice had assumed her very best Queenly Attitude.

"Right then, tails together. Are we *All Four One?*"

The cats linked tails, lightly this time, and chanted their assent like a war cry.

"All Four One and One Four All!"

"So remember," Rufus continued as they disentangled themselves, "we have to stick together. I'll lead the way. Rico, you bring up the rear. Your Royal Highness, you and Jake can go in the middle. Off we go. Ouch!"

The fossilised tree had obviously come back to life. It was waving its stone branches around and hitting anything in sight. Rocks whizzed through the air, missing Beatrice by inches. She jumped and dodged and yelped as one hit her front paws. Fossilised trees had not formed part of her Special Skills training.

"We have to get the timing right – ouch!" shouted Rufus, rubbing his head and jumping to one side to avoid another thwack. "This tree has knocked out a good few explorers before us. We need a diversionary tactic."

"I guess I could tell it a few jokes," said Jake, rolling away from the missile onslaught. "Hey, what d'you call a fossil that just lies there? Lazy bones, geddit? Ha ha! Ow!". A large stone hit him hard on the bottom.

"Seems like this fossil ain't got a sense of humour. Why was the tree stiff? Cos it was petrified. OK, OK, I give in!" The stones were hailing down thick and fast. "Rico, your turn. Where've you gone?"

The answer came as a huge crash from the far side of the tree. Maverico had fallen over while standing on one leg trying to do the Tree pose. The fossilised tree branches turned immediately in the direction of the sound and started flinging themselves at him. Quick as a flash Rufus leapt past the tree trunk and into the gaping hole.

"That's it, I'm in. Great tactic, Rico."

Maverico rolled over just in time to avoid a beating from the branches coming his way. Then he jumped up and began performing cartwheels while the missiles rained down.

"Quick, off you go Bee." Jake gave Beatrice a good shove and before she knew it she was standing next to Rufus in the tunnel entrance.

"Well done Rico," Jake shouted. "Guess I'm goin' to have to eat my words 'bout you bein' marvellous. What ya gonna do for me? How's about a nice, noisy forward roll, maybe?"

But Maverico launched himself into a spectacular series of back flips which took him neatly out of reach of the bombardment while Jake dived into the tunnel entrance to land beside Beatrice and Rufus.

"But how are we going to get Rico in?" asked Beatrice.

"Oh, he'll manage somehow," said Rufus. "He's not called Maverico for nothing."

The next moment Maverico took another huge leap and threw himself upwards into an overhanging elm tree. A few minutes later there was a sound like stones falling a short distance away. While the branches turned their attention to the new threat Maverico swung himself through the air, dropping neatly into the hole on top of Rufus.

"I say, old man, well done! Just like Tarzan." Rufus looked up at him with a new respect. "What did you find to throw?"

88

Maverico shrugged. "I just asked ze squirrels for a few spare nuts."

"The squirrels gave you their nuts?" Jake was incredulous.

"I say to zem either I throw ze nuts or ze squirrels. Simple. And zey are very 'elpful."

"Right, first part of the mission accomplished. Now on to the next," said Rufus. "There's no time to lose."

"Thought you said that in here there's no time at all," said Jake.

"What's Time?" asked Beatrice.

"Ees time to find out," said Maverico.

CHAPTER 11

OUT FOR A SPIN

The tunnel seemed remarkably ordinary, except to Beatrice, who had never been down a tunnel before. It was not large, but it was quite big enough for a cat on all fours and fairly easy for a kitten. The floor was made of beaten earth and rocks. The walls were mostly stone except that, when they looked closely, the stone was full of fossilised remains – jawbones, teeth, spines and ribcages and large snail-like creatures which reminded Beatrice of the spiral bat-map.

"Take heed, gentlemen and Princess," said Rufus. "These are the bones of the poor creatures who failed to make it through. They say that this was where The General lost his leg."

"That so?" Jake began examining the trapped bones more carefully. "Which one of these do you think it is? Can't see no ginger ones there. And this one here's far too elegant." He pointed to a long thin femur which was sticking out at a slightly odd angle. Beatrice thought she saw it wiggle as he spoke.

"That looks like one of the deer to me," said Rufus. "At least The General managed to get free, even if he does only have three legs now. Most of these other creatures weren't so lucky. They are now forever lost in Time."

Beatrice shivered. No one had actually explained to her yet what Time was, but she was absolutely sure she didn't want to get caught there if this was what happened to you.

90

"Don't seem that tough to me," said Jake. "That old fossil of a tree was nothing to write home about and I can't see nothing untoward here neither. Come on, let's get moving."

"Right-ho!" said Rufus a little too loudly. "On the double!"

But Jake was mistaken. As soon as they set off, they found the tunnel was untoward in all sorts of ways. With each step they took it jerked and lurched violently and they ended up falling over. If they stepped backwards, it reared up before them like a huge horse. If they tried to go sideways there was hardly any room and if they so much as touched the walls the fossilized jawbones started to open and close threateningly.

"Jeepers, that was a close shave," said Jake, whisking his tail away just before one of the jawbones snapped shut on it. "Think we'd better sit still for a moment."

"I am sitting still," said Beatrice, "but something's moving."

"I say, you're right!" Rufus put a paw out to steady himself. "Thought I just had a touch of vertigo. It's the tunnel going round."

"O my giddee auntie, not again," wailed Maverico, as the tunnel speeded up.

"Don't feel like a tunnel – more like a giant plughole and we are just goin' down an' down," said Jake, gloomily. "Best thing I reckon, Bee, is to lie flat on the floor. And hold on to your markings, cos I'm guessin' this thing is gonna fly."

And then everything moved so fast that it all disappeared at once. For a long time – or maybe it was a short time since there was no one there to tell the time – there was nothing at all. No tunnel, no walls, no cats, no fossils, no outside, no inside, no forward, no backward, no past, no future. And then, in the blink of an eye, or the flick of a whisker, everything slowed down again and all was as before.

Well, not quite as before. Maverico's legs were all tangled up. Rufus's beautiful golden tail was now a series of knots. Jake was completely upside down and Beatrice's markings had wound themselves tightly round and round her in a series of concentric circles so that she could hardly breathe.

"'Elp me, I am completely spiralised," wailed Maverico.

Rufus put his tail to one side as he helped to pick Maverico's limbs apart.

"Definitely beats Disneyland," said Jake, turning himself the right way up.

"What happened there?" gasped Beatrice, turning round and around as she tried to loosen her markings so she could breathe more easily.

"More to the point, what's happening here?" said Rufus, gazing into the far distance.

The tunnel was gone. In front of them lay an open, unfamiliar landscape. There were trees – a bit like the playful monkey trees, though much bigger. But this was definitely not a wood. Huge spiky bushes and giant green ferns grew among open scrubland. Enormous rocks reared up from the flat earth. In this world it was daytime. The sky overhead was the deep blue of a lake and even the sun looked younger and yellower, bigger and brighter than it had before.

"Wow!" said Jake.

"By Jove!" said Rufus.

"Magnifico!" said Maverico.

"It's so bright. Do you think this is where my colours are hiding?" Beatrice asked Jake quietly.

"Don't know 'bout your colours Bee. Don't know 'bout Candy neither. Isn't she supposed to be here? What d'you reckon Roof? Which way now?"

From somewhere around his neck Rufus brought out the bat phone. He blew hard on it and set it clicking. "Rufus to bat battalion. Are you reading me? Rufus to bat battalion. Come in please."

"I don't know why he does that. They can't hear his voice, only the clicks. Anyway, it's daytime here, I should think they'll be asleep. Oh, watch out!" Jake dragged Beatrice out of the way just as a gigantic bat, bigger a cat, swooped over them. It knocked Rufus and Maverico over before heading off over the horizon taking the batphone with it.

"What was that?" Beatrice gasped in amazement.

"Well it's not one of our bats, that's for sure," said Rufus. "Must be the watchman for this place. Or maybe one of The General's spies. I guess we really are on our own now. Oh Rico, do pull yourself together."

Maverico had dived under the nearest tree and was shaking from head to foot. "I tell you these bats, they are ze fiends not ze friends. I think I cannot go on."

"Well you sure as hell can't go back," said Jake. "Wouldn't know where to start. The tunnel's gone now anyway, so let's get moving in one direction or another. What say we follow the sun?"

Rufus looked rather subdued but he nodded his agreement and they set off across the plain. It was strange being out of the wood. The trees here were too far apart to provide safe cover and the cats felt exposed and vulnerable. Beatrice looked up fearfully from time to time at the blue sky, but it was empty. The sun was hot on her fur. The scrubby grass was hard and the thistles pricked her paws. She missed the soft green moss of the Wildwoods. And she was also hungry.

"I'm starving," she wailed.

"Me too," said Jake. "Just wondering if there's any rabbits around."

The four cats stood still for a moment searching the bushes for signs of anything that might provide a dinner. Beatrice was just thinking longingly of her food dish in the attic, regularly restocked by The Lady with precious delights, when she became aware of the ground trembling beneath her – like a thunderstorm breaking deep inside the earth.

"That don't sound like no rabbit," said Jake, "and...uuuh that don't look like no rabbit to me neither."

Between the bushes, an enormous creature was approaching. It was as tall as a tree, with a long neck, a huge head and a thick tail trailing behind. The Thing walked for the most part on all fours, rearing up on its back legs every now and then to eat some leaves from the treetops or a bit of gigantic fern.

"Quick, up here," said Rufus running across the scrub to the nearest tree. They scrambled up the tree trunk till they were as high as they could go. "We'll have to camouflage ourselves as best we can."

Beatrice's markings shook so hard with fear that they turned themselves into bark-coloured ridges as she clung to the tree trunk. Maverico hung upside down pretending to be a bat and Jake wound himself around a branch like a big black python. Rufus could not think of a disguise so he simply imagined that he was a lion, fluffed up his ginger coat and tail as much as he could manage with all the knots still in it from the Time Tunnel and hoped he looked scary enough to put the monster off.

It did not have the desired effect. The creature headed straight towards them. They watched, trembling, as its mighty head came level with theirs. Enormous jaws opened and closed, crunching on the lower leaves and branches. The teeth came nearer and nearer to where Rufus was crouching, trying to make himself look large and threatening at the same time as small and inconspicuous. The creature drooled with satisfaction, flicked its huge tongue and caught him right on the nose.

"Ouch!" Rufus tried to finish the exclamation with a fearsome roar. The monster opened its enormous mouth wide and belched loudly. And then it made a strange cackling sound. It took a few seconds before the cats realised that it was laughing.

"Oh my goodness, that's a first. I've never seen a batcat before. Or a mini lion. Or a black furry snake for that matter.

Oh dearie me!" The creature chuckled again and then addressed Jake directly.

"Actually you look more like a caterpillar than a python dear, very cute. And as for you, sweetie," the monster turned its head to where Beatrice was clinging to the tree trunk, her markings frozen with fear, "why, you remind me of a rather tasty fungus, hanging there like that. Quite delicious. Now I don't know who you all are or what you are doing here, but you're lucky that I'm a vegan, which is more than a lot of folk are around here. The name's Dino, by the way."

"Wow, that's original," said Jake, unwinding himself from the branch. "Spose your second name's Saur and all?"

"Why, how did you guess?" Dino appeared surprised. "Are you one of those, what are they called now? Oh yes, clairvoyants."

"Don't know 'bout that, but I sure can see into the future." Jake's confidence was beginning to return.

"Really?" said Dino. "How lucky! In that case would you happen to know whether it be worth my while hanging around this part of the world for a bit? It's just there's this rather lovely lady I'm interested in. Name of Dinah. And well, I've always wanted kids and a settled future, you know? A few gingko trees, the odd giant mushroom, the simple life. Do you think that's possible?"

"Let me see now, I reckon you'll be fine." Jake screwed his eyes up and tried to look as though he was concentrating hard. "Only thing you've got to worry 'bout is ice. You see any ice approaching and you get the hell out just as fast as you can."

"Ice, you say?" Dino looked puzzled. "Don't think I've ever come across ice before. Is it an animal? Or a fish perhaps? But I'll certainly keep a lookout."

"That's enough Jake," Rufus interrupted. "Take no notice of him, Dino. He's making it up. But I wonder, would you happen to have seen some other cats coming this way? Perhaps with a little kitten? A very pretty kitten. Name of Candy."

"Well now, I don't recall anything unusual. But there is that one they call The General. Only three legs. Dirty, meat-eating rascal. Of course, being a vegan myself I am very sensitive to smell and suchlike, especially the smell of dead flesh."

"Of course," the cats chorused, looking a bit embarrassed.

"A meat eater, you say?" Maverico did a back flip out of the tree onto the ground and stood in front of the giant herbivore, waving his front legs in a theatrical display of disgust. "That ees truly a tale of 'orror." He flicked his tail for emphasis. "I must then meet 'im and eat 'im myself, this disgraceful General. I give to 'im a dose of 'is own tablets, no?"

"Well, almost," said Rufus with half a smile.

"I don't know exactly where he is, I'm afraid," said Dino. "But I think you need to go over this plain then turn right by the side of a lake, and through the swamp. That could be a bit tricky, I guess for the likes of little chaps like you. Just keep on going and eventually you'll see a huge cliff in front of you. It's full of caves. I'm afraid they might have taken your friend there.

"Now I don't mean to be rude but there's a very rare fungus I need to catch before old Bronto gets there and demolishes it in one sitting. So if you'll excuse me, I wish you all the very best, and I do hope you find your little friend. Chow for now!"

And with that Dino lifted his huge legs and began to run. The earth trembled once again beneath his feet and branches snapped loudly as he raced through the trees. The cats looked at each other.

"What you know? 'E speaks Italian, zees veganosauraus. Arrivederci, Dino," Maverico's voice echoed across the great plain.

But Dino was already out of sight. Before them lay the new world – or the old world, depending on your point of view. But where in that world was Candy?

CHAPTER 12
MUDDY WATERS

The four cats followed Dino's instructions. They walked across the plain with the hot sun beating down on them. Once an enormous bird swooped from the sky and they ran for cover. In the distance they heard strange cries and the occasional loud shriek which made them shiver with fear. But otherwise the landscape was eerily empty. They saw no rabbits and no more veganosauruses, or any other sauruses, for that matter. And no Candy.

They walked mostly in silence. The skies were wide and disappeared into the horizon in a blue-grey haze so they could not make out where the one ended and the other began. With no hills and no woodland to break up the landscape this world seemed vast and empty, as though it was just waiting for someone, or something, to come along and fill it up. Beatrice felt very small and yet very conspicuous.

The cats had been travelling for what seemed like ages and yet they did not appear to have got anywhere at all. The horizon, or the sky, depending which you thought it was, just moved further away. And the strangest thing of all was that every footstep felt like the first one.

"I suppose you only know you have gone a long way because of the time it takes you to get there," said Rufus thoughtfully.

"And how much your legs hurt." Jake yawned and sat back on his heels, stretching his front legs as far as they would go.

"These paws are beginning to feel real sore, so I reckon we must have walked for miles."

"I know I've come a long way because I remember things," said Beatrice. "I remember the giant bat and Dino and all the different trees and cactuses. And there was that huge scary bird we thought was going to eat us. Remember?"

"I remember, Piccolina." Maverico was practising his martial arts moves as he went along. "'Ees called the Terror Dactyl because 'e ees so terrifying! And I remember how I fought 'im off." He brought one long leg up to shoulder height and did a high kick. "We are ze four muscateers, no?"

"That's weird, Rico, cos I distinctly remember you trying to get away from it and racing up those trees like there was no tomorrow," said Jake mischievously.

"Perhaps there is no tomorrow," said Rufus, staring into the distance, glassy-eyed. "Perhaps we, too, are lost in Time."

Beatrice looked at him in alarm. Where was the calm, confident cat she had come to trust? Perhaps Time had a way or worming itself inside your head and making you see things differently. Well it wasn't going to get inside her head.

"Actually, I know there's a tomorrow cos I remember it," she said bossily. "It's when I was in the attic and then Jake came and we had a party. And then Candy was kidnapped. And the day after tomorrow we all went to rescue her."

"All a bit deep for me guys," said Jake. "But I'm thinking that you know you've come a long way because what you look at changes. Or maybe it's the way that you look at it. And wouldn't you know, I never saw this swamp coming."

The other cats followed his gaze. Sure enough, where just one second ago there had been a dry plain, now there was a marshy mess.

"This here looks like the swamp that old Dino talked about. Feels like it too." He dipped one paw cautiously into what looked like a puddle. When he drew it out again it was covered with mud and green slime. "Wonder how wide this is. And how deep."

"I wonder what lives in it." Rufus was eyeing the vast expanse which had opened up before them, where patches of reeds grew tall and brown water steamed in the sunshine.

"Ees the swamp monster I think," said Maverico. He began to tremble all the way up his legs and along his spine. "I come from an 'ot country. I cannot abide ze damp. We 'ave to find another way."

Beatrice began to get irritated.

"For heaven's sake, pull yourselves together. We have to find a way across because of Candy." She looked around. "What about those old tree trunks lying in the water? Maybe we could use them as a sort of bridge."

"Nice idea, Bee." Jake had broken off one of the thick reed stems and was busy making holes in it with his incisors. "Only problem is, them there tree trunks have got rather hefty jaws."

Beatrice looked again and saw gleaming eyes peeping out from the tree bark, just above the water level. Then one of the trunks split in two to reveal a set of huge, jagged teeth.

"Crocodiles!" said Rufus. "And I think there is something else under there too by the way the waters are bubbling up."

"I told you," shrieked Maverico, whose voice was getting higher by the minute. Beatrice was too embarrassed to speak at all. Only Jake seemed unperturbed. He had found a small stick and was poking it through one end of the reed while blowing hard on the other. It made a strange whistling sound.

"Really, Jake. I need you to concentrate," Rufus rebuked him sternly. "This is serious."

"Certainly is, Roof," Jake agreed. "And so's this here reed flute. Listen!" He played a rather rudimentary scale. Rufus was just about to deliver a lecture on military discipline when Maverico let out another huge wail. "Ze swampie. Ees alive!"

By now the filthy waters were rolling and heaving like a witches' cauldron. Soon a series of oily, black loops appeared above the mud, followed by an almighty sucking sound and then a plop, so loud it was more like an explosion as the creature's head broke the surface of the swamp.

Beatrice's markings were so terrified that they leapt back on top of Jake and temporarily blinded him. But the others saw it clearly. It had a thick neck which waved wildly a small head with huge flat triangles at either side and blood-red eyes which glittered like rubies. Its mouth opened like a gaping wound, displaying a forked tongue which flicked and darted repeatedly.

"Ees the monster," shouted Maverico, but his voice was drowned out by a dreadful hissing sound from somewhere inside the creature's throat. The sound had a strange sinuous quality. It wormed its way down the cats' ear canals and into their brains, whispering of fiends and ogres, dogs and demons and a thousand secret fears which had no name.

Rufus shook his head and flicked his ears over and over to try and dislodge the sound from inside his head. Maverico did a cartwheel and then a handstand to achieve the same effect, but the hissing continued. Beatrice decided to join her markings and attach herself to Jake who alone seemed unfazed by the creature in front of them and was busy playing with his reed pipe as if nothing was happening at all.

"You're right Rico, it's a sea-serpent," gasped Rufus between ear flicks. "Or perhaps I should say a swamp serpent. Just the sort of thing I hoped the bats would have alerted us to. But of course the bat phone is now in enemy hands. I wouldn't be surprised if The General himself hadn't sent this thing. Obviously now he knows our exact coordinates."

At this point the serpent reared up to its full height, which was at least as tall as Dino, and launched itself at the four muscateers. They leapt back just in time.

"I think we're going to have to regroup," said Rufus, trying to sound in control, as though he was not shaking all over.

"Eees fly or die," said Maverico.

"I wouldn't be so sure of that," said Jake. "Now out of the way you lot and let the cat see the rabbit. Or should I say, let the serpent see the Cat!"

While the other cats cowered, Jake found himself a grassy knoll at the edge of the swamp. Then he sat down, took up his instrument and began to play. The reed pipe made a weird, thin sound and the tune was not really a tune at all, or not one that Beatrice could make out. But the serpent recognised it. The hissing stopped, the glittering eyes glazed over and the flailing neck and head became perfectly still. Jake played on, never taking his eyes off the creature in front of him.

"Jake, a snake charmer! Who would have guessed?" Rufus whispered to Beatrice. "Reminds me of when I was serving in India. Didn't think he'd been there though."

Jake did not respond. He seemed to be in a world of his own where there was only himself, the serpent and the music. Very slowly, he began to move, swaying gently from side to side as he played. The serpent swayed too, hissing a little at first, and then becoming quiet, undulating gently like a calm sea, so that eventually the two of them – the small cat and the huge reptile – moved together to the strange, exotic tune. Beatrice's markings moved along with the music, forming and reforming exotic patterns – spirals, circles, figures of eight – while Rufus and Maverico watched in silence.

"All well and good Jake," said Rufus after a while. "But you're going to have to stop cos we have to find a way across."

"Hold your horses," Jake muttered out of the corner of his mouth. "Just a lil' longer to make real sure."

A few minutes later he stopped his playing and took the pipe from his mouth. The serpent froze in mid-air, still as a sculpture.

"That's the one," Jake slapped his lips which were dry from all the blowing, and gave a slow, satisfied yawn. "Gotcha now, baby. Proper trance state. You're all mine."

The serpent remained motionless.

"Just like musical statues," said Beatrice in delight. Musical statues had been one of the games Sheba approved of – as long as the statues were royal, like the sphinxes.

Jake addressed the creature directly. "First of all I command you to tell me your name."

There was a slight pause. The serpent flicked his tongue very slowly from side to side as though waking up from a deep sleep. Then he began to hiss equally slowly. "C…c…c…c…c…"

"Come on old chap, spit it out." Rufus was not entirely comfortable with the way Jake appeared to take command.

"Watch it, he don' listen to you Roof. I's his only master now," said Jake with a satisfied grin. He looked at the serpent. "Now you try again. Tell me your name. And make sure it's your real one."

The tongue flicked again, a little faster this time. "C…c… c…c… Cedric," it whispered, rather than hissed.

"Well now C…c…c…c… Cedric," Jake imitated the snake's manner of speech. "You know who I am. You know that I'm your master, right?"

The serpent nodded its head on its long neck and hissed. "Yesssssss…ssss…ssss."

"So me and my friends here, we need a lift across this swamp. Now do you think you could do that without drowning us?" Jake blew a few more notes on his pipe for good measure.

The snake swayed again from side to side and nodded quite gracefully. "C…ccc…ccc…certainly, Mas…sss…ster."

"OK, now we need you to bend your head right down here so we can climb onto your shoulders. Not of course that you have shoulders, being a snake." Jake thought for a moment.

102

"Tell you what, if you can make a few nice curves with your back so they are out of the water, my three friends can jump on them and stay safe."

"Delighted to s…s…s…serve you, O Great One." Cedric bowed again and did as he was told.

"Ok Rico, you go first. You're best at jumping, so you go to the end."

"Of course, Maestro." Maverico bowed low in mock obeisance. His fear of swamp monsters had disappeared, as though he too had been hypnotised by the reed pipe. He climbed onto Cedric's head and shimmied along the scaly neck then jumped from one shiny black hoop to the other till he was right at the serpent's tail end. He waved to his friends. "Now tell me, Grandissimo, 'ow else my I s…s…serve you?" he asked, saucily, and bowed again with a flourish.

"That's enough Rico," Rufus said in an attempt to reassert his own authority. "I'll go next, then the Princess and then you last, Jake, at the head."

And so the cats settled themselves on the beautiful, glistening curves which stuck out of the muddy swamp. Jake perched right on top of Cedric's head and began to play his reed pipe again. The huge serpent's head rocked a little from side to side as it started to move and Jake was hard pushed to keep his balance. But that was the least of their problems. Because in order to move forward Cedric had to curl and uncurl his long body which meant that, just as the cats were getting comfortable, the curves they were sitting on straightened and disappeared underwater. Fortunately others rose up to take their place, so the cats had to jump from one to the other as they went along – and timing was everything. Only Jake got to stay relatively still at the head.

Maverico had a great time doing somersaults and cartwheels and generally showing off as they travelled. Beatrice thought the whole thing was a fine game, though she became very cross with her markings which kept jumping ahead of her. But Rufus, whose balance was not so good, found the whole thing rather stressful. Once he missed it altogether and fell right into the swamp and had to be rescued by Maverico who hauled him out of the water by his tail, leaving him covered in mud and slime.

When they reached the other side of the swamp Jake decided that Cedric should turn himself into a slide to allow them to disembark.

"Up! Up! Up!" he commanded, until Cedric was almost completely vertical and the cats were clinging on to his scales with their claws for dear life.

"Now Cedric, think Downward Dog. That's it, make a nice V-shape. Get that head right down, hips in the air…what you might call snake-hips hey? Now come on you lot. One, two three – and slide!"

And so, with much hilarity, the four cats slid all the way along Cedric's shiny, scaly neck, over the top of his head and onto dry ground. Cedric remained frozen in his Downward Dog until Jake blew on his pipe and told him to move. Slowly, the serpent raised himself up.

"Thanks Cedric," said Jake. "Now you can go off and play with the crocodiles or Nessie or whoever your friends are round here. When I next blow on this pipe you'll be your old self again and you won't even remember this. Until I call you again of course. Then you will come. We may need your help sooner than you think."

"Yess…ss…sss…sss…ss…ir. Thank you sss…ssss…ssss… ir," Cedric replied, in his humblest hiss. "Ssss…sorry to sss… sss…sssee you go Masss…sss…ssster."

With that Jake blew one long single note on this pipe. Immediately the snake's glazed expression disappeared, replaced by the deadly, glittering gleam. The black hoops writhed and undulated wildly, the mouth gaped, the tongue lashed and the dreadful insistent hissing began again. The cats watched in relief as Cedric slid away into the depths of the swamp. They stayed watching as the mud closed over him and long after the last bubbles of air had disappeared.

CHAPTER 13
WHEN NOTHING HAPPENS

"Are we nearly there yet?"

Beatrice was getting bored with walking. They seemed to have gone for miles and yet the sun was still in the same place in the sky, which was rather dispiriting. There were no caves or cliffs in sight and no sign of Candy either, or the dreaded General. On top of that, since meeting Cedric they had had no adventures to distract them along the way. Beatrice liked adventures, though, as Jake pointed out, this might be because so far they had all turned out rather well.

"I suppose it depends on where 'there' is," said Rufus who had become something of the philosopher of late. "And where here is."

Beatrice was finding Rufus's intellectual angst a little irritating. Jake explained that Rufus was used to knowing exactly where he was and where everything else was and planning accordingly.

"Typical military type. Always needs the exact coordinates. What I call living by numbers." He yawned and stretched before continuing his stroll. Beatrice had never seen Jake hurry for anything.

"Never was no good at sums myself. Which is a bit weird cos now I'm happy just to be *sum*where and know we'll arrive *sum*time." He chortled to himself. "No good with figures see, but pretty hot on words."

Beatrice was not convinced that this explanation was any more helpful than Rufus's musings. And Maverico was no better. Ever since he had hidden from Dino by pretending to be a bat he had become quite obsessed by them. He had lost his bat phobia altogether and now spent most of the time leaping from tree to tree in an attempt to fly.

"Beware, ze BatCat," he yelled, as he fell to earth once more, this time landing on Rufus, which did not go down too well.

Thank heavens for Jake, thought Beatrice, though even he had been uncharacteristically quiet of late. For the first time since they had left home, Beatrice thought longingly of her tiny attic and the Lady and the cardboard box full of Christmas tree decorations. She was even beginning to miss Sheba. At least all those Catiquette lessons had given her something to think about.

"Guess this is the hardest part of any journey," said Jake, as if reading her thoughts. "You can't see where you've come from no more. And you can't see where you're going neither. You just got to Bee and keep on believing."

"Believe in what though?" she asked in a rather stroppy tone of voice. Sometimes Jake's habit of playing on her name got on Beatrice's nerves.

"In Candy of course, that she's OK and we'll get there in time – or, er, whenever." Jake stopped himself from starting another discussion about the nature of Time. He could tell Beatrice had had enough of that. "And then you've got to believe in yourself of course."

"That's a stupid thing to say." Beatrice was really grumpy now. "I don't have to believe in myself, I just am."

"Gee, you certainly are!" Jake grinned in a way that Beatrice, feeling as she did, interpreted as patronising. "But who are you exactly?"

"I'm a Princess, of course." Beatrice tossed her head impatiently. "*The* Princess of the Wildwoods, though no one seems to appreciate that."

"Well, that's true BayBee, or course. But who are you on the inside? We all know there's days when your markings are, shall we say, out of sorts. And those days no one would recognise you, let alone know you were a Princess." Jake's tone was gentle, despite his words. "Why I'd say there's days when you don't even know yourself who you are. And when you don't know who we all are neither. Like now, for instance."

Beatrice's mouth was open and she was about to make an indignant reply, when she caught sight of her markings. She was used to seeing them wriggle around and rearrange themselves and generally misbehave. But now they were not even on her body at all. They were hovering in the air, almost as though they did not belong to her. Except that, like her, they were quivering and shaking with irritation and anger. More worryingly, where the markings had been, – where Beatrice had been – there was now nothing. Not even an outline. Just empty air. Jake was right, without her markings she could not see herself at all. But where could she have gone? Was she with her markings? Or somewhere else entirely? Panic rose inside her.

The markings moved further and further away, then rose right up into the air and began to separate out into their different colours. The gold markings flew off to Rufus, where they wrapped themselves into a beautiful scarf around his neck. Some of the black ones headed for Jake and became absorbed into his own thick, glossy coat, which became even thicker and glossier. The remaining black markings teamed up with the white ones and zoomed over to Maverico where they arranged themselves into a rather fetching polka dot waistcoat.

"Help," Beatrice heard herself scream from somewhere. "Help me! I've broken down. Or I've broken up! I've disappeared! I'm invisible! Look!"

To her amazement – as well as her horror and fury – the three cats ignored her screams. They carried on walking and chatting in a desultory fashion, just as though nothing was happening at all. Nothing, thought Beatrice, from wherever she was. That's me, then. Without my markings I am nothing and nowhere. Why can't they see me or hear me?

"Help!" she screamed again.

But all she heard were Jake's laconic tones. "Looks like we go left here."

The mystery of it was that, although she appeared to be not there – or indeed, although she did not appear at all – she seemed to be travelling at just the same rate as before. Jake, Rufus and Maverico walked and she moved along with them. But how could that be?

Was she walking? She could see no legs. And, assuming that her eyes had disappeared along with her head, what exactly was she seeing with? Yet she could definitely see them all. She just could not see herself. And they apparently could not see her either. Or else why would they ignore her?

Despite the fact that she was invisible Beatrice realised she could still think and feel. But it was like she was in bits. All over the place. Wherever her markings were, it seemed, there she was.

Once, Rufus put up a paw and stroked his golden scarf, apparently not realising it was actually Beatrice. Beatrice felt his touch. It was warm and lovely and reassuring. Yet Rufus did not seem aware of her at all. But then he took hold of the scarf and flung it around his neck and Beatrice felt giddy and disoriented and rather worthless. And still Rufus did not address her – even to apologise.

The next minute Maverico decided to undo the buttons on his polka dot waistcoat and Beatrice had the scary sensation that she was unravelling somewhere deep inside. It was like he had taken her apart and just left her there, hanging open, with all her insides on show to the world, and no dignity or privacy left at all. Where, she wondered, did he think that waistcoat had come from in the first place? How could he not have guessed it was part of her?

But then she felt another bit of herself snuggled right up inside Jake's chest and she heard the soft, regular beat of his heart and the gentle rise and fall of his breath. Jake would never hurt her, or throw her carelessly around without permission or consideration. Here, at least, she felt safe and loved, though still decidedly ignored. She cuddled into him and felt his strength surround her. No matter that he could not see her or that she had gone to pieces. Here, close to his heart, she was whole again.

And it was from this position – or rather from these three positions – that Beatrice became aware that Something was finally happening.

CHAPTER 14

WHEN SOMETHING HAPPENS

It was Rufus who spotted it first. His beautiful golden tail doubled in size and stood up like a brush.

"I say, chaps, what do you call that?"

Jake and Maverico followed the direction of his eyes. So did Beatrice, except nobody noticed her. About a hundred yards away was yet another bizarre creature. This one was taller than a horse, but much broader. Its legs were so thick and gnarled they resembled the fossilised tree except that, like the rest of the creature's body, they were covered all over in wool. On its head were two enormous horns – not side by side, but one in front of the other.

"Probably someone called Charlotte or Mavis, based on previous experience," said Jake, trying to keep their spirits up.

"Very funny, Jake." From the tone of his voice Rufus obviously thought it was anything but funny. "Do you think it could be some sort of giant sheep?"

"Could be," Jake thought for a moment. "'Cept it moves more like a rhinoceros. Them horns definitely fit."

"What's a rhinoceros?" whispered Beatrice from her three different positions, only of course nobody heard her.

"Rhinos, they're real mean," said Jake, which at least partly answered her question. Beatrice did not think it looked mean. It was lumbering around in a rather desultory fashion, nibbling on a bit of grass here, a bit of bush there. And it did not seem to have seen them. *Perhaps we are all invisible, not just me,* thought Beatrice.

"Ecco amigos, this ees a woolly bull!" Maverico's eyes were shining. "At 'ome, I dance often with ze bulls. Ees called a Paso Doblé." He broke off a branch from a tree and started waving it around like a sword. "Fear not! Jake, was ze 'ypnotising 'ero. Me, I am ze marvellous matador! With me, even ze woolly bully 'as no chance."

He started lifting his legs high and stepping out in a most peculiar fashion. Jake and Rufus could not help laughing and even Beatrice found herself giggling. She noticed her markings vibrating with laughter in their various locations. She watched Rufus put up a paw to adjust his shaking scarf. What on earth did he think was going on? And as for Maverico's new waistcoat, its spots were bouncing up and down like rubber balls, yet no one remarked upon it. As if it was perfectly normal.

Then Maverico did the weirdest twisted walk they'd ever seen and all the cats, both visible and invisible, collapsed into giggles. They were laughing so much they didn't notice that the woolly bull, or giant sheep or weirdo rhino, had come closer and finally spotted them. They looked up just as steam began to pour from its nostrils. For once Beatrice thought there might be some advantages to being invisible.

"I say," said Rufus, "it's about to charge. Quick, move!"

But Maverico had acquired an uncharacteristic courage. "Ze matador, 'e never runs," he said, clicking his heels together and turning his hips this way and that in a very bizarre manner. "But I need ze cape. And some music. Pronto!"

"Well, I don't think the reed pipe's the thing for the Paso Doblé, but I can do a bit of beat boxing and Roof here's got a good voice," said Jake.

"As for the cape," Rufus frowned for moment. "Maybe this is one for the Princess."

"Come on Bee, let's be 'aving you," said Jake, just as though he knew she had been there all along.

He brought up one of his back legs and gave his chest a good scratch, right where Beatrice's black markings were. It was a most unpleasant sensation, like being thrown up in the air and falling to bits at the same time. Some of the dislodged markings floated back to Jake's comforting chest which made her feel a little calmer. The rest wafted aimlessly about in mid-air.

Rufus put his paw up to his throat. "Time to unwind, I think," he remarked, to no one in particular. He undid his lovely scarf and shook it out and the gold markings, too, flew up into the air. Beatrice heard herself shriek in alarm.

Maverico threw his spotty waistcoat to the ground. "Ze matador, 'e goes bare chested!" he announced, dramatically.

The spots floated up from the earth like black and white bubbles. Beatrice felt herself fizzing like champagne. When the spots met the gold and black markings they exploded and then all the colours wove together to form a large, striped cape.

"Looks just like a flag," said Jake.

It was alright for them, thought Beatrice, who was feeling distinctly nauseous, as well as confused and disoriented. They did not have bits of themselves exploding and stretching and rearranging themselves without so much as a by-your-leave. They were not left hanging in mid-air like an old rag. They were not invisible and striped at the same time.

"I command you as your Princess to stop this now," she shouted, apparently silently, because no one replied to her or obeyed her command. Maverico took the cape and waved it about so vigorously that she had to shut her mouth to stop herself being sick. Only the bits of her still tucked cosily inside Jake's chest felt safe and warm. She tried to concentrate on those and ignore the rest.

"OK Rico. It will have to be Los Toreadors, I'm afraid. Only one Roof knows the words to," Jake announced.

And so, in the middle of a prehistoric plain, Jake began his beat-boxing, Rufus began to sing and Maverico began to dance. As for Beatrice, one moment she shook up and down with the rhythms of the dance inside Jake's chest. The next she felt herself wafted up and down and side to side in the cape by Maverico till she had no idea even what *was* up or down anymore, or indeed what was the music and what was the dance. Or what was her and what was Maverico. They were all one and she was no one. And yet, from inside Jake's chest part of her regarded the whole thing with fascination.

She watched Maverico as he stepped in time with the music. She noted, with some surprise, how powerfully he strode across the plain and how elegant and commanding he was as he waved the cape right in front of the woolly bull. For a second she lost focus as it began to charge at them. It came nearer, nearer, then at the last minute Maverico flicked the cape into the air and the creature galloped onwards, apparently unable to change direction. Beatrice's stomach flipped with fear as Maverico swivelled round and the cape came down again. The strange bull seemed confused, but then it too turned and readied itself for the next charge. Beatrice was giddy, not just with the movements of the cape but with the effort of moving her focus from where she was within the cape to Jake's comforting chest.

But as the dance continued and the rhythmic charges happened again and again, Beatrice found herself more and more within the cape, surrendering to the melody of the music and the graceful, fearless movements of Maverico. Who would have thought that there could be such freedom in letting go? In being nothing and yet being a part of everything. Was this what the wind felt like, Beatrice wondered, as she was wafted aloft in the cape and waved once more to the ground.

But the woolly bull was not giving in so easily. Just as Rufus was beginning the song all over again the creature charged unexpectedly and lunged right at Maverico. Maverico pulled the cape away and stuck out the branch he was using in place of a sword. The woolly bull tripped right over it and lay on the ground, steam still pouring from its nostrils, while Maverico stood, victorious, the branch jabbed into its belly, his cape waving triumphantly.

"Kind sir, please don't kill me." The voice was high-pitched and surprisingly soft. "Please don't hurt me. I was really enjoying that. I haven't danced in ages. Not since the last Ice Age in fact. And then, of course, it was skating really. Much harder to stop of course."

"Identify yourself," Rufus commanded, imperiously.

The creature bent her front legs in what looked, to Beatrice's trained eyes, like a clumsy sort of curtsey. "Good day to you, kind sirs. My name is Myrtle and I'm a woolly rhinoceros. Not actually a bull at all. But I do enjoy pretending from time to time. A girl needs a bit of fantasy, wouldn't you agree?"

"Myrtle, of course, I should have known." Jake rolled his eyes. "That's all we need, a rhino with a personality disorder."

But Maverico waved his cape one more time and bowed low.

"You are truly the phantasm madam. And I am indeed honoured to be your partner in the dance."

What about me, thought Beatrice, who had come down from her lofty visions of being one with everything as soon as the music stopped. *I think I was pretty important there too.*

As though reading her mind, Jake took the cape from Rico and held it to his chest. "Reckon we've all got to say a big thank you to Bee, for, well, Bee-ing here, doncha think? What you did there was pretty amazing, Sweet Bee."

As he spoke Beatrice experienced the most extraordinary sensations. The markings in the cape were pulling apart and the ones in Jake's chest were too. Then in an instant they all joined together and she was back. Properly back. In one piece. In one place. Her eyes were in her head, her feet were on the ground and her tail was swishing angrily from side to side. And as for her markings, well her markings had arranged themselves in the most bizarre manner. Her dainty face and front legs were pure white, a black waistcoat covered her chest and shoulders, complete with white polka dots. Her bottom half and legs were black except for the paws, which were white, and an elegant gold stripe wound round her neck and along the back of her spine. It was one of the strangest designs she had ever seen. And yet it still felt like coming home. Like being whole again.

Beatrice was both puzzled and relieved. But even as she began to relax into the comfort of her markings there was also something else. Just a hint of regret. A feeling of limitation. A sense of loss. Of finally being somewhere and no longer being everywhere. But she was not going to let them know that.

"How would you know what was happening or whether it was amazing?" Beatrice said indignantly.

"Oh, my dear, you'd be surprised what I know." Jake put up a large black paw and gave her a little cuff across the ear. "Don't mean to say I can do 'em myself though. What you did there was quite extraordinary. Me with my plain black, I couldn't hope to do those things. Nor Roof. And even Rico, he's got two colours but he can't just move them around any old how, or let 'em go like you can."

"But you forgot about me," Beatrice was shouting now. "You didn't hear what I said, or talk to me. It was like I was INVISIBLE!"

"Not exactly invisible," Jake's voice was gentle, "but you was tired and beginning to zone out, and you are still only little, so we sort of shared you between us. It's safer that way sometimes. It means we can protect you better. Bit here, bit there. We share the load and you get to rest. Of course we could only do that because you have the gift."

"What gift?"

"Why the gift you've just given," replied Jake mysteriously. "Could call it magic, could even call it sacrifice, I s'pose. I don't think you even realise what you just done."

"No," said Beatrice, "and I'm not sure I want to do it again either – whatever it is."

She settled down for a quick wash, but as she licked her markings to a beautiful glossy finish she felt them move under her tongue like strange wild animals, with a life of their own. Who were they? And, come to think of it, who were Jake and Maverico and Rufus? And Candy and Gangsta and Grubsta? All these cats who had mysteriously turned up in her life and turned it upside down. Where did they come from? Why were they here? And were they a gift or a curse?

CHAPTER 15
IN PERFECT TIME

Myrtle was becoming a bit of a problem. Well, Myrtle and Maverico to be exact. The problem was that Myrtle was completely obsessed by her new dance partner. Indeed, she seemed to have fallen in love with him. That was the only thing that could explain the way she skipped about him, putting her head coquettishly on one side and rubbing her horns against him in a rather suggestive manner.

"Never thought I'd see a rhino skip," said Jake, grinning despite his irritation. "Even a woolly one."

But Myrtle just would not give in. "Maestro," she pleaded, in her softest, girliest voice, "just one more dance."

Then she would charge at Maverico playfully. But, of course, he had no cape now that Beatrice was fully restored to herself. So all he could do was step aside, with a flamboyant stamp of the foot. At first Maverico had enjoyed the attention, but now he was getting bored with it.

"For me the conquest is all," he confided to Beatrice as they walked, skipped and stamped their way across the plain. "After that, I need ze fresh challenge."

"Well, maybe your fresh challenge can be getting rid of her," said Beatrice unkindly. "She's slowing us down for one thing. And she'll never be able to climb up the cliffs to the cave – wherever that is." She gazed around her with a sigh.

Just then they heard heavy footsteps racing towards them from somewhere in the bushes to their left. They looked up

118

in alarm. Who could it be this time?

"Quick, jump up on me," said Myrtle, no longer coquettish, but back to her strong, primeval self. "I'll take care of this. Just lie across my back. Whatever it is, it won't notice if you lie still."

The four cats needed no encouragement. They jumped up and arranged themselves neatly on top of the woolly rhino. Maverico straddled her neck and lay with his paws around Myrtle's throat and his head peeping through her horns, which made her smile dreamily. Rufus and Beatrice were lying sideways across her back like a saddle while Jake hung his long body over her hind quarters.

"I have to say, this is rather cosy," said Rufus, snuggling into Myrtle's woolly coat. "Reminds me of an Arran sweater I once had."

"Reminds me of them palomino ponies out West, with all these colours," said Jake, digging his claws into her rump to stop himself falling off. "Just don't move too fast or we'll fall off."

The footsteps got faster and nearer. Beatrice, now the bravest of the bunch, raised her head and peeped out from her hiding place. "Actually, we don't need to hide," she said, "it's only Dino."

Sure enough, the veganosaurus was coming towards them at quite a pace. If Beatrice had not been so excited she would have noticed the look of panic on his face.

"Hi Dino!" she called. "Have you met our friend Myrtle?"

"Oh my dears, you must leave here immediately!" Dino's voice was taut with terror. He turned to the woolly rhino. "Delighted to meet you Miss Myrtle and I do apologise, but this is vital. We have to go now, this minute. Jake, you were right. The ice is coming. Look!"

They looked to the far horizon, in the direction from which Dino had come.

"By Jove, he's right! Something's happening!" Rufus exclaimed.

Before their eyes, the landscape was changing. The brilliant blue skies had become leaden grey. The air was thick with fast approaching snow and the dark rocks and the green bushes were disappearing beneath a white blankness.

"I'm cold," said Beatrice, snuggling into Myrtle's warm fur. "What should we do, Roof?"

The temperature was dropping fast. Maverico's teeth were beginning to chatter.

"We 'ave to go. We will be ze snow angels. Frozen to death."

"There's no point in running. Look, it will be here in seconds." Rufus's voice was surprisingly firm. "Myrtle, Dino, you go now. You will be faster than us. No, that's an order," he said, sternly, as they appeared to protest.

He turned to the others. "Now then, if we are to rescue Candy there has to be a way. There's always a way. You know what we need to do. Quick, before our tails freeze!"

So the cats slid from their hiding places and while Dino and Myrtle ran for their lives the four cats wound their tails together once more, all wondering if this would be the last time.

"*All Four One and One Four All,*" they chorused, weakly.

When they opened their eyes their tails were hanging with icicles and Jake and Rufus had white patches of ice on their fur.

"I don't want to unwind," said Beatrice trying to hold back the tears that were turning to ice. "Not if we're going to die. I'd rather be together."

Jake looked at her fondly. Then looked at her again. And again.

"Who was it said there's always a way, Roof?" he said, through chattering teeth. "Look at Bee!"

Rufus looked. "Good Lord! Unwind, quickly. Now!"

There was a lot of crackling as the ice fell apart and the tails unwound.

"Bellissimo!" said Maverico.

"What?" asked Beatrice anxiously. "What's wrong?"

"Nothing, kid. Nothing at all," said Jake. "You've just got what I call a way with you."

Beatrice looked down and saw that her markings had re-arranged themselves into a series of arrows all pointing in the same direction.

"So we go right," said Rufus, shivering, looking at her chest.

"No, is ze left!" Maverico argued, standing behind her.

"It's the same you mumpties," said Jake through a mouth that was nearly completely iced up. "Now let's move before we freeze to the spot. Come on, all in a line behind Bee."

The cats did as they told and formed a neat line.

"But I can't see my arrows any more in this snow," wailed Bee who was at the front.

"We'll shout up from behind then," said Jake.

"I can see them. I'll shout up," Rufus was at his most military. "On my count…And…Left!…Turn!…Now quick march!"

The four cats stepped out in unison, except for Maverico who insisted on doing a salsa step. When they looked up they were surprised to find a huge mountain in front of them which had definitely not been there before. They marched towards it and after just a few steps they became aware that the snow had stopped altogether. Then Jake realised that Bee's arrows were still pointing left.

"Think that means we have to keep turning," he said. "Guess it's left again buddies."

"On my command," insisted Rufus. "And…Left…Turn!"

The cats dutifully turned as one. This time they found themselves at the edge of a huge lake where swans glided and fish leapt and graceful trees bowed their branches to the water.

"Wonder if Cedric's under there somewhere," said Jake, thoughtfully.

121

"Can't wait to find out, I'm afraid," said Rufus. "Have to follow the markings wherever they lead. And it's left again. Turn!"

The cats turned together once more. Before them was a beautiful beach with a warm sun beating down.

"Ees near my auntie's 'ouse, I think," said Maverico. "I 'ave to call in and see 'er."

"Sorry old thing, can't stop here," said Rufus, eyeing Beatrice's markings again.

"I'm getting dizzy with all this turning," grumbled Beatrice. "What if my markings have got it wrong?"

"Ain't no other way to go, that's for sure," Jake said. "They look pretty clear to me."

"Ees my turn now. I will lead," Maverico insisted. This time Rufus, who had secretly begun to mistrust his own instructions, did not argue.

"To ze left, on my beat. Now!" Maverico turned with a flourish. The other cats, though, were a bit late.

"No, no, you are out of time, my friends. We 'ave to go back and do it again!"

"Can we be out of Time?" asked Beatrice, who was now both dizzy and confused. "Where would we be then?"

"Where we are now I guess," said Rufus. "To be honest everything looks a bit hazy."

"Can't see a thing," said Jake. "Rico's right. Let's do it again."

So the cats shuffled back to the right and tried again. This time they managed the steps correctly and landed all together.

"Zat's it!" Maverico was excited. "Ees perfect time zis time."

They looked down at their paws and up at the world around them. No ice. No snow. No swamps or monkey trees. The sun felt warm on their backs. Beneath them was lush grass and overhead white woolly balls of cloud moved against a clear blue sky. Around them not quite so white woolly sheep grazed peacefully.

"It's like having bits of Myrtle everywhere," said Beatrice. "I do hope she and Dino are alright."

"Fancy a dance, Rico?" asked Jake, mischievously.

"But where are we?" wondered Beatrice, whose arrows had disappeared and whose markings were now a series of concentric circles.

"Only one way to find out," said Rufus and set off in the direction they were facing. Beatrice, Jake and Maverico looked at each other, then took a deep breath and set off after him.

CHAPTER 16
DEAD AND ALIVE

This time the walking was different. The path changed from mud to stone to grass and back again, and the landscape on either side of the path changed too, from barren soil to lush pasture and then to heather moorland. Yet behind them and before them the view remained the same. Always they saw the same woodland, bordered by rocky cliffs and dotted with caves, where Candy was, no doubt, being held prisoner.

They walked through hot, dry deserts where scorpions scuttled under rocks and caravans of camels loped, led by dark-skinned men in long robes. They walked through villages of round, rough stone where people wore animal skins and cooked their tea over an open fire. They walked through timber-built towns with narrow streets, where women leaned out of windows to empty their buckets and the cats had to jump out of the way to avoid being soaked. They walked through farms where sheep grazed and cattle ambled home for milking and through mill towns where machines clacked and whirred and clogs clicked along cobbled paths.

Sometimes people threw them food. Sometimes children laughed and pointed at them. Sometimes they cursed them and threw stones at them and the four cats had to escape quickly. They saw no more veganosauruses, swamp serpents or woolly rhinos, but plenty of dogs and occasionally a wolf or even a bear.

One of the strangest things was the sun, which rose and set with alarming speed. Sometimes a new sun came before the old one left. Sometimes there were two or three suns together in the sky. At night the moon waxed and waned like a live creature. One moment it was full, the next it was the merest sliver of a shine. Often the sun and moon were out together. All in all the cats never knew day from night or one minute from another or, indeed, one century from another. But despite walking till their paws were raw, they never seemed to actually get anywhere.

One day, when they had had to run for what seemed like miles to escape a pack of ravenous wolves, the four friends collapsed, breathless, under a bush.

"Sorry chaps, I'm game for adventure but this is ridiculous," gasped Rufus. "We've no way of navigating by the sun because it changes position all the time."

"Can't tell the time from the moon, neither," observed Jake. "I suppose this is one hell of a history lesson, though."

"What's history?" asked Beatrice, whose markings had taken their cue from the sun and the moon and were now continually waxing and waning, so that Maverico complained they were giving him a migraine.

"Well now, I'm not sure I know that anymore," said Jake. "Used to be things that had already happened. But all that seems a long time ago now."

Beatrice thought about Sheba and how she'd talked about pyramids and palaces in Egypt as though it were yesterday. "Maybe that's why my mother got so confused," she said.

"Well, I don't like to admit it, but maybe the old dame knew more than we reckoned."

"Ah, excuse me."

The four cats turned their eyes upwards towards the voice. An elderly man stood before them. He had grey hair with gold-framed spectacles and was smartly dressed, in a black jacket over a neat waistcoat and dark trousers.

"I heard you were looking for a cat. Me too, in a way. I'm sorry, allow me to introduce myself. Schrödinger's the name.

Erwin Schrödinger. I'm wondering if you've found her. It could be important, you see, for my experiment. Although if you'd seen her you'd know one way or the other, I suppose."

"Know what?" asked Jake, stepping out from under the bush.

"Is her name Candy?" asked Beatrice.

"I don't know," Mr Schrödinger replied. "I suppose it could be. I hadn't thought about a name."

"Ees a spy cat! I spy 'im with my own eyes!" Maverico had assumed the en garde position.

"Fair point, I suppose," said Rufus. "How do we know you are not a spy, sent by The General."

"No, no, I'm not a spy. I'm a scientist. Physicist, actually."

"When it comes to the physique I am ze undisputed champion!" Maverico had puffed himself up to four times his normal size and was flexing his muscles for a fight.

"Not that sort of physique." The old man smiled and tried to give Maverico a gentle pat. "Ouch!"

Maverico's teeth had ripped a sizeable gash in Mr Schrödinger's hand. He rubbed it hard.

"No, you see, the thing is, this cat I am talking about, she's locked in a box with some poison gas that might or might not have been released. No one knows. And no one can see her. So no one knows if she is alive or dead. And until someone sees her to verify it, it seems she is both. Alive and dead at the same time. So in a way it is a bit like you and your, what was she called, Candy?"

"Candy's not dead!" Beatrice shouted. "She's been kidnapped by the Bad Cats and now she's with this General person. So he can see her, and so can they, even if we can't." She looked over at Jake for confirmation. "He's not going to poison her is he?"

"'Course he ain't." Jake sounded confident. "She's far too valuable for that. When they find out they gotten the wrong kitten they're gonna wanna swap her."

He looked over at Mr Schrödinger. "Don't suppose you've got an experiment to swap kittens in a box, have you? Like one of them card tricks? Only joking Bee," he added hastily. "We'd never swap you, dead or alive."

"Forgive me, sir," said Rufus. "But just exactly how long has this cat been locked in this box? Perhaps someone should call the animal protection organisations. It seems likely she would be dead of starvation by now even if she hadn't breathed in the poison."

"Ah, yes, there is that." Mr Schrödinger took off his glasses and wiped them carefully with his pocket handkerchief. "But then there is the whole question of time. As St Paul said, now we see through a glass darkly." He wiped his spectacles again and put them back on. "But sometimes I think all we have is now." He blinked benignly.

"Then it seems to me you should be letting that poor cat out, like, *NOW*," said Jake.

"What cat?" said Mr Schrödinger.

As one, the four cats rolled their eyes to heaven.

"Oh, I'm so sorry, it was just a hypothesis, a sort of thought experiment. It's all about possibilities, d'you see? Not about a real cat at all. Not like your little Candy, though there are some parallels of course. I didn't mean to distress you." Mr Schrödinger coughed apologetically.

"Now, if you'll excuse me, it's a bit noisy here and I need to get a move on before the train comes through. So I'll bid you good day and I do hope you find your companion. If you do, perhaps you'll be so good as to let me know. It could be relevant." And with that he strode away.

The cats stared after him.

"Was he for real?" asked Jake.

"For the love of God, don't you start," said Rufus. And for once, despite their tiredness and anxiety, they all burst out laughing.

"He was right about the noise though," said Beatrice. "Funny we didn't notice before. But what on earth is it?"

An immense banging and clattering was coming from somewhere quite nearby, along with a deep rumbling sound that made their paws vibrate and their bellies turn over.

"Whatever it is," said Jake, "it sure don't sound too happy."

"Ees a dragon?" Maverico, who had been a bit lost during the conversation with Mr Schrödinger, suddenly perked up. "I am ze dragon slayer extraordinaire. I trained in South America on ze…"

"And I'm sure you've got the certificates to prove it," Jake interrupted, rather irritably. "And the medals. But from what I hear, you might be a bit late. Sounds like something's on its way out. Whoops!"

A great metal contraption was clanking and hissing its way down the hill towards them.

"Yippee, looks like a train!" Jake was excited.

"Quick, out of the way," shouted Rufus.

The four cats ran back and hid under their bush as the machine chugged past. At the front was a dirty black engine with steam coming out of a funnel. Behind were a dozen or so open carts, all joined together. The carts were loaded with slabs of heavy stone. Some were so huge and wide it was hard to imagine how anyone had managed to lift them onto the trucks. Others were smaller boulders, piled up high.

"By Jove, it's a quarry. So that's what we could hear," said Rufus. "And this is the railway. We must be back in the Wildwoods."

"Only there ain't been no quarries here for a hundred years," Jake pointed out. "And no railroads neither."

Just as the last cart went past and the din began to die down Beatrice saw Jake start and point to something. Rufus looked up, then stood rigidly to attention and Maverico bowed so low he appeared to be doing a handstand.

"What's up?" asked Beatrice. "What's all the fuss about?"

But apparently her markings knew the answer to that question, even if she did not, because they were already bending and bowing and stretching and bowing again – a little like Maverico.

"It's him," gasped Jake, "ain't it?"

"Never thought I'd see the day," said Rufus, wiping a tear from his eye with one paw as he looked after the departing carriage.

"Ees a miracle! Ees back from the dead!" said Maverico.

Beatrice followed their gaze. Just as the last cart rounded a bend she spotted a large, handsome tabby cat perched on top of a big stone slab. As she gazed the cat lifted one paw, very elegantly and waved, as though beckoning them to follow. The next moment he was lost to view.

"Who was that?" asked Beatrice, surprised to feel tears in her own eyes even though she did not recognise the figure who was provoking such a reaction. "He's very handsome, whoever he is."

"That, my little Princess, is your father," said Rufus, gravely. "That is King Leon."

CHAPTER 17

GETTING SOMEWHERE

The cats stood in silence, listening to the sounds of the train dying away in the distance.

"But how can King Leon be here?" asked Beatrice, eventually. "I thought he died or decided to stay in the city and eat cream. Or just left us."

"Well, Bee, that's what we thought too, if we thought anything." Jake's voice was thick with emotion. "But then we thought dinosaurs were extinct. And we never thought woolly rhinos could dance."

"Perhaps they are all dead now. Frozen to death." Beatrice sighed, thinking of poor Dino and Myrtle and the dreadful ice that had covered everything.

"Or perhaps they are both," Rufus interjected. "Dead and alive, like Mr Schrödinger's cat. Until someone sees them, then they are dead *or* alive."

"And we ain't seen 'em, so they ain't dead." Jake was emphatic. "And, come to think of it, we've just seen Leon so he ain't dead either."

Beatrice's head was spinning almost as much as it had done in the Time Tunnel.

"Maybe it's not just who sees them but when they see them and where they are looking from." Rufus was getting into his philosophic mode now. "I mean, if you look at the same object from different sides, or from above or below, it can look completely different. But it's really the same. So perhaps

Time's like that that. What you see depends on where you are in Time, at the time, so to speak."

"Ees right," said Maverico. "I am scared of ze bats. I am not scared of ze bats. Ees both true. Depends eef you go forward or backwards in Time." He did a forward and a backward roll to illustrate. "So when time ees a-mixed up, I can be both at once." To illustrate, he decided to do the four-legged splits.

"Oh no, one of you is enough." Jake rolled his eyes at Bee. "Thing is, you lot can cook up these theories but we have to live where we are now or, should I say, *when* we are now. Wherever and whenever that is. And Old Leon, he was definitely there, so he's definitely here, somewhere. I vote we go look."

"What about Candy?" wondered Beatrice.

"Maybe Leon has information we don't," said Rufus. "I suggest we wait for the next train and follow him."

"Gee, I love a railroad." Jake was grinning so much his whiskers were turned up at the ends. "Reminds me of the Wild West. We need to find out where it stops to load up."

"Must be back there somewhere," Rufus nodded in the direction the train had come. "Let's take a look."

So the four muscateers turned and walked back along the railway line. They passed through some fields, climbed up a grassy slope and crossed over a big stone bridge. On the other side was a platform of sorts, with a ramshackle stone shed at the back of it.

"Well," said Rufus, looking around him in surprise, "we seem to have left the rural idyll firmly behind us."

"What's a dyll?" asked Beatrice, but her voice was drowned out by hammering and crashing noises, much like they had heard earlier. She scampered after the others who were already on their way to investigate.

Since they had escaped the Ice Age the cats had become accustomed to the way the landscape changed around them.

One moment it was all fields, the next it was factories. They had seen huts made of wattle and daub and massive cathedrals under construction. Some mornings they had woken to the clatter of wheels on cobbles, others to the sweet song of birds, hidden in hedges or forests. But this was something new.

All around them was noise and industry. They could see men and boys in filthy clothes, hauling huge stone boulders from the depths of the earth. The air was thick with gritstone and the labourers coughed the dust from their lungs as they worked.

"My nose tickles," Beatrice shouted to Jake, joining him and the others under an old wheelbarrow.

"My whiskers an' all," he yelled back. "Sounds like they're killing something over there."

Above the crashing and banging something was groaning, loudly. The sound echoed across the surrounding hills and bounced back again with an eery force. It was a fearful sound, like an enormous creature being torn in two. Beneath their paws the cats felt the earth vibrate, resist and finally surrender.

"Look, over there!" shouted Rufus, pointing with his paw to a rocky outcrop a few hundred yards away as a slab of stone the size of a small cottage split from the rock face and slid to the ground with a great sigh. The men stopped what they were doing to cheer. Beatrice looked at the poor, broken rock face and felt quite sick.

"So this is definitely our quarry then," said Rufus.

"Guess it all looks different," Jake was sniffing the ground curiously. "No trees now. Or should I say no trees yet?"

"That looks a bit like where my house is, I mean was, I mean will be," said Beatrice, who was getting more and more confused about Time. She was staring out beyond the stone shed towards a row of tiny cottages with stinking outhouses and washing hung out to dry in the grit and dust.

"Same place, different time," Jake replied. "Should be used to it by now. Thought we were getting somewhere for once." He sounded uncharacteristically downhearted.

"We are, we are going to rescue Candy!" Beatrice tried to make her voice jolly and encouraging. But then she didn't know what to say next. So she said nothing and just looked at Rufus, hopefully.

"That's the spirit, Your Royal Highness."

Her markings wriggled with pleasure at Rufus's approval.

"We just have to get on the next train and follow King Leon," he continued. "We should be able to do it while they are loading up. Look, there's one coming in now." An old train was pulling into the platform, with much wheezing and clanking.

"We 'ide in the carriages, no?" Maverico leapt from their sheltered position and balanced precariously on the edge of an empty wagon.

"Watch out! Don't let them see us!" snapped Rufus. "And we don't want to be in one of those things when they start shovelling the stone in either. I say we go for the engine end. Should be nice and warm there. Jake, you go first, since you know your way round these railroads."

Jake perked up. "Actually that engine's real rusty. Nice camouflage Roof. If you jus' roll in the dirt a bit to dull down the old ginger, you'll be OK up there. No one'll notice you."

"They won't notice me either," said Beatrice triumphantly. "Just look what I've done!"

Somehow Beatrice's colours had mixed themselves up together so finely that the black and white and gold had all melded into a perfect, uniform, browny-grey. She was unrecognisable and almost invisible against the stone.

The three adult cats stared at her in silence.

"D'you do that yourself, Bee?" Jake asked, quietly.

"Well of course I did. I mean who else would?" Beatrice sounded very pleased with herself. "Well, I didn't really *do* anything. I just sort of imagined it and they did it all by themselves. Aren't they clever?"

"Not as clever as you my dear," said Rufus, gravely. He looked at Maverico and Jake, who didn't look as excited as Beatrice thought they should be in the circumstances.

"What? What's wrong now? What have I done?"

"Nothing, my dear. Absolutely nothing." Rufus's voice was kind and soothing.

Jake looked at him. "Guess it won't be long now then?"

"What won't be long?" Beatrice was getting annoyed.

"Till you grow up proper." Jake shook his head sadly.

"That's good isn't it Jake? So why are you looking so miserable?"

"Nothing, lil' Bee. Jus', well, time flies sometimes."

Beatrice looked up at the skies in alarm. No one had mentioned that Time had wings.

"I can't see anything flying. But don't worry, Jake, if it comes anywhere near I'll catch it. And kill it if I have too. If it makes you feel better."

She rubbed her dainty stone-coloured head against his big black one and licked his ears. Then she decided, while she was about it, to give them a quick wash, since they were quite grubby. She was so intent on her task she didn't notice the way Jake's eyes glistened with tears.

* * *

The train began to puff and grumble, like an old man waking from an afternoon snooze.

"Pronto, ees a starting," Maverico shouted. "Everybody hup!"

The cats crept aboard, careful to avoid being spotted. Rufus sat on top of the rusty engine. Jake found himself a cosy spot near the coal hole, where he disappeared from view in the blackness, while Maverico climbed underneath one of the wagons, wound his long legs round one of the metal supports and hung upside down like a bat. Beatrice settled down on a large stone slab and became almost invisible, although not in the way she had done before. This time she had done it herself, deliberately. It felt quite exciting.

There was a lot of banging and shouting and hauling and lifting as the last of the stone was loaded. The metal creature shook and wheezed and whistled. Finally, it gave a big hoot, like a giant owl, and set off along the hillside. The machinery clanked, the engine panted and the brakes squealed.

"How will we know when to get off?" she shouted through the din. But nobody heard her.

Above her she could see Rufus struggling to stay balanced on top of the engine. Meanwhile Jake, huddled in his coalhole, was having a quick forty winks, despite the noise. She wondered how Maverico was doing on the undercarriage. Then she caught a glimpse of his long tail peeping out from underneath one of the wagons and waving jauntily so she knew he was OK.

They had been going uphill fairly steadily for a good while when suddenly everything turned upside down. The engine cab, which had been above Beatrice, was now below. The wagons, which had been below her, were now above and the train was gathering speed. They were heading down the hillside. She felt herself begin to slide and wedged her bottom into the corner between two slabs of stone to keep steady. Below her, she heard Maverico's whoops of excitement followed by a "Jeepers" as Jake woke from his slumber in the coalhole and banged his head. Beatrice was beginning to enjoy the excitement when she saw the ginger form of Rufus tumbling through the air on her right. The movement of the train had been too strong for him to hold his balance.

"Roof!" shouted Beatrice, but it was too late. The train was speeding along and Rufus was long gone. "Jake?" she called.

"Sure thing Bee, I seen it. We need to go after him. You ready to jump?"

"Of course!"

"Great! You too Rico?" There was no reply.

"Too late Jake, he's gone."

Maverico was somersaulting down the hill with his long legs sticking out in all directions, apparently unable to stop.

CHAPTER 18
THE FALL

"I can't see them anywhere."

"Guess ol' Roof could be miles away by now. That lil' train was goin' at quite a rate down that hill."

Beatrice and Jake were standing on the edge of the woodland. They had jumped together, not long after Maverico. Jake had insisted they wait till they got to a grassy bit so they would have a softer landing.

"I don't know what time this is," said Beatrice, trying to sound as though she knew what she was talking about, "but it's very pretty. Look, the leaves are gold. And they're all over the ground too. But there's only one sun in the sky. And no moon. So what does that mean."

"Guess we must be back in real time again – whatever that is." Jake breathed in deeply, sniffing the musty woodland air. "And all this here, why that's what I call Fall. Think they call it Autumn over here."

Beatrice considered this information. "So is that why Rufus and Maverico fell off then? Same as the leaves – because it's Fall? Will Maverico have gone golden like Rufus by now? And what about us?"

Jake chuckled. "Not sure I'm ready to be no golden boy jus' yet. But I forget, you're only a few months old and you've been stuck in that attic all the time, so you ain't seen no seasons before have you? Well, not the way they're supposed to be, any road." He paused for a moment, looking uncharacteristically thoughtful.

"Way I see it is, the year, it's jus' like a long version of the day. Winter season is like the night when everything's asleep – apart from the badgers and the bats I s'pose. Spring is like sunrise and everything's fresh and new. Then Summer's like high noon. Warm and full of life. And when Nature gets a lil' tired and sleepy you have Fall, which is like sunset. The colours are pretty similar too, all soft and glowin'. So much better than the tinsel and tacky baubles in your Christmas box, doncha think?"

Beatrice gazed up at the trees, which were tired out but still ablaze. She looked down at the leaves already asleep on the ground, their colours softening into the earth – browns and greens, ambers and oranges.

"So are all these my colours too? Like you said, you know, when I was born?"

"These colours and more Sweet Bee. Why, these are the colours of the wood and you're goin' to be Queen of the Wildwoods one day. So of course they'll be yours. Same as the yellow daffodils in Spring. An' the bluebells in May. An' the moss that goes emerald when the sun touches it. All yours."

"I think I like the gold best for now." Beatrice raced into the wood and started leaping about in the autumn leaves. They made a lovely crisp sound which made her ears giggle. Her gold markings separated themselves out from their stone-coloured disguise and moved up her back and over the top of her head.

"If I lie flat now, you can't see me!"

Jake laughed. "True enough. An' ol Rufus, he's completely disappeared."

Suddenly their cheerful mood disappeared as well.

"I hope he's alright, Jake. He did fall off a way before us. Maybe he saw King Leon and went after him," suggested Beatrice. "He'll be better disguised than me in all these golden leaves. Shall we shout?"

"Better not," said Jake. "Don't want to alert The General and his crew. Need to take care. Thing is…"

"What Jake?"

"If Rufus don't show up easily in these colours, then The General won't neither, him bein' a ginger an' all too."

The two cats considered this for a minute in silence. Then Beatrice spoke. "I don't get who this General is anyway. I know you said he's head of the Bad Cats. But how did that happen? Surely he can't be that bad."

"Oh, he's bad alright. Cruel and dangerous, you ain't no idea."

"Then give me some idea. What makes him bad and us good? If we *are* good, that is." Beatrice thought Sheba might have her own opinions about that.

Jake spoke softly. "The General, he weren't always bad, no. The opposite in fact. He was handsome and brave and strong. Put Rufus in the shade, I'm tellin' you. That's why King Leon made him head of the army whose job was to keep the Wildwoods safe. But then, what with Sheba an' all, Leon took his eye off the ball an' The General, he saw his chance.

"He was always ambitious and when Leon went he started lording it over us all. But that wasn't good enough for him. He didn't just want these Wildwoods now, he wanted them forever, for all time, past and future. That's why he headed for the Time Tunnel. Claim the kingdom, like."

"But we went through it and we're alright. Well, I mean, I don't think we're bad – are we?" Beatrice's eyes were big black saucers.

"We were lucky Bee and we were travelling to rescue Candy, not just for ourselves. That's one of the things that helped keep us safe, see. But The General, he was out for himself so he didn't have that protection. He got his leg trapped. Couldn't get it out again."

"So is his leg lost in Time then?" Beatrice shivered, thinking back to the bone-lined walls.

Jake nodded gravely. "It's not just that he's only got three legs. Plenty of cats manage like that. But The General, he was so used to being handsome and strong, he took it very hard. Like a part of his soul was missing, not just a leg. Maybe that's more to do with how he lost it and where.

"Either way, he just changed overnight. When he came back he found himself an old iron rod, guess that'll be from the quarry days, and he used that for support. Wouldn't go nowhere. Just hid up in his cave, leaning on that rod, feeling sorry for himself, thinking bitter thoughts. And, as I heard it, his flesh started to grow right round that old piece of rusty metal, till it became a part of him."

"A false leg, you mean?" Beatrice asked.

"Yup, only not so false anymore." Jake shook his head. "Seems like the rod itself started to grow too, only in-side – leastways that's what they say. It grew until it reached his heart and then right round his heart and then inside his heart till that became iron too. That's when he became truly bad. And now, seems like he don't feel nothin' – well, nothin' good. No warmth, no softness." Jake patted his own warm, soft belly in appreciation.

"No love either then?" Beatrice thought back to her own lonely, loveless days in the attic, before Jake and Rufus and Rico and Candy. "The poor old General."

"Hard to feel sorry for a piece of metal," said Jake. "'Specially one that moves and kills and even tortures, from what I hear."

Beatrice shivered again. A terrible scream filled the air.

CHAPTER 19
STICKY MOMENTS

"'Elp! 'Elp! Eesa captured me! The octopussy of the woods! So many legs! I am stuck. I am bound. Ees finito!"

Maverico's terrified wails came from high above where they were standing and a little further into the woods. Beatrice was about to rush straight off to rescue her friend when Jake put a large flat paw across her shoulder.

"Hold your horses, Bee. Don't know what we're getting ourselves into here. Need to go careful. Tell you what, I'll go first."

So Beatrice tucked herself in behind him and the pair crept through the leaves carefully. They moved slow and low, peeping out every now and then for a swift look round and up. Maverico was still shouting, which at least meant he was still alive.

"Never thought I'd find myself behaving like a rabbit," Jake muttered, peeping up from behind a large fern. "Still you learn a thing or two about prey animals when you're a hunter."

"I see him! I see him!" Beatrice's whisper verged on a shriek. "There, look!"

"Well, I'm jiggered," Jake sat right up on his hind legs. "Looks like he's hanging in mid-air."

Maverico was high up in a tall beech tree and appeared to be suspended between two big branches, though it was impossible to see what was actually supporting him. Whatever it was was also binding his arms and legs, which were wrapped tightly round him. It was as though he were covered in invisible bandages.

"Rico?" Jake's voice was low and urgent. "What's going on?"

"Ees the octopussies, I tell you. Lots of zem. So many legs. With claws. 'Elp me please!"

Maverico's voice shook with emotion.

"Don't remember no octopussies in these woods, Rico. Leastways, they wouldn't have no claws, neither." Jake looked around him edgily. On balance he preferred monsters he could see. At that moment a shaft of sunlight glanced through the half-bare branches.

"Oh, that's so beautiful!" Beatrice was staring upwards in awe. "It's just like the wispiest white clouds have come down from the sky."

Jake followed her gaze. All around them were networks of glistening fine silk threads. They hung from the branches and dangled from the dead leaves. They swung in huge swags in the spaces between the trees, trembling and sparkling like rainbows in the sunlight.

"Can't believe we couldn't see those before." Jake shook his head admiringly. "And just look at the shapes of 'em!"

There were triangles and funnels and towers and orbs, wide woven blankets and great flat circles that looked like lace doilies. The filaments were so fine they would have been invisible were it not for the low angle of the autumn sun. Either side of Maverico they could now make out layers of silk supports. Only the craftsmen themselves remained invisible. Jake burst out laughing and shouted up at his hapless friend.

"They're not octopussies, you idiot. They're spyders. They're called that cos they run a spy network. A sort of intelligence service for the wood-wide web. Armies of 'em by the

142

look of it. And they've trapped you like an enormous black and white fly. You're inside a sort of spyder silk stocking."

Maverico's wails became louder. "Ees no laughing matter. Like zis I am ze spyder supper."

"But it's so beautiful," breathed Beatrice. "It's like a whole city. Like a fairy city from one of Sheba's stories."

"Well, I'm glad someone appreciates us."

The voice was thin and high-pitched with a strange musical quality. It appeared to come from somewhere inside the tree canopy.

"We'd appreciate you a sight more if we could see you," said Jake, peering through the overhanging branches.

"That is not what most folk say." The creature's voice had developed a sharp edge.

"People run from us, they scream when they see us. They throw us out of windows or flush us down plugholes…." The tinkling voice became fainter, like fairy bells heard through fog. Then it gathered strength again. "All we are doing is trying to keep their houses clear of flies. And they call our cobwebs dirty!" They could hear sniffing, as though the creature were crying.

"Well, ma'am, if you are actually a ma'am, that's people not cats, if you don't mind my saying. Cats is different," said Jake.

"All the same," chimed in Beatrice, "if you kidnap cats and string them up so they can't move you can't expect us to like you for it."

"Ees evil, ees crazy!" Maverico's wails began again overhead. "I am ze cat, I am not ze fly. Zere are no flies on me."

"Please," said Beatrice, remembering her manners, "let us see your face, then we can talk to you properly. I am sure you are not that ugly."

The creature sniffed loudly but stayed hidden and said nothing. Beatrice had an idea. "Look, if you show yourself, I promise to make myself really ugly too. So then we can both be ugly together. Not that you are of course, I'm sure – ugly I mean."

"Nice one, Bee." Jake's expression was a cross between grumpy and proud. "Think you can do it?"

Beatrice gave him a look and he fell silent. This was partly because her eyes had the steely quality of Sheba, and partly because of the transformation that was going on in front of him. Beatrice's face had become a splodge of shapeless black and gold so he could only just tell where her nose and eyes were. The rest of her was a filthy, blotchy grey. Her Royal Highness Princess Beatrice just looked like a dirty, dark bruise. She grinned with delight at Jake's horrified expression.

"Come on then," she called triumphantly to the invisible spyder. "You can't be worse than me." It had the desired effect.

"Goodness! What a transformation!" the spyder trilled. "That can only mean one thing. You can't be…you must be… Oh dear, I'll be right down."

"What about me?" wailed Maverico from his spyder hammock above.

"This ain't about you Rico."

Jake was still staring at Beatrice when he became aware of a tiny, brown creature lowering itself towards them on a fine silver thread. As it moved the tinkling took on a more musical quality, like something tripping down the scales on a xylophone. Eventually it settled itself on a broken branch just about level with their eyes and hooked its thread around a loose piece of bark.

"Good morning to you my friends, the name's Darius, so no, not ma'am." The creature turned to address Jake directly. "I am the moderator of the wood-wide web, which your friend referred to just now. I can't say I am at your service though until I know what you are about. More than my job's worth, I'm afraid." He finished with a peal of nervous laughter.

Darius looked at Beatrice. "Now that's what I call ugly."

"Thank you." Beatrice was pleased with her transformation. More importantly, this was the second time her markings had done what she had asked them to. "But I think you do yourself a disservice with regard to your looks. You aren't ugly at all. You're just…" she thought for a moment, "…angular. Except for your body which is very, well, big and fat and round. A bit like Jake here without the fur."

"With a few more legs attached I guess, and the eyes in a different place." Jake was beginning to relax. "Y'know, just cos you're a Princess, don't you go getting above yourself. Else you might end up up there with Rico."

Maverico let out another howl of rage and anguish.

"So it's true then?" Darius eyed Beatrice warily. "Those markings and everything. You're Beatrice?"

"Your Royal Highness, the Princess Beatrice, to you," Beatrice retorted huffily. Then she looked down at her filthy, ugly markings and laughed. "Though I guess Beatrice will do for now. Tell me, how do you make all those amazing shapes? You couldn't do it all yourself."

"Of course not your Royalness," said Darius. Beatrice sighed in exasperation and looked at Jake, who just winked back. "There's hundreds of us, thousands of us. Maybe hundreds of thousands.

"Most of the time we do our own thing. Very independent, we spyders. And of course we're competing for flies and the like. But we also act as a task force to protect the wood, to sort of bind it together. These webs really are the most efficient intelligence network. Anything moves in these trees, we know about it. The webs shake and the vibrations pass from one to another. Which is how we knew about you and your friend up there.

"When it's something big it's one out, all out. Like an army really. Come on lads, lasses. Show yourselves to your Princess."

Darius tugged lightly on the thread that was attached to his belly. Beatrice heard a faint peal of tiny bells all around her and then the spyders appeared from everywhere. As Darius had said, there were thousands of them, all spinning their threads as they dropped through the air until they formed a fine silk curtain all around the cats.

"That's better, now we can't be observed," said Darius with some satisfaction.

Beatrice looked in wonder. There were spyders of all shapes and sizes – dainty ones with tiny heads and long legs, large fat ones with legs so hairy they could have belonged to a dog, red ones, brown ones, microscopic ones, shiny ones, dull ones, even stripy ones.

"Gee, that's kinda neat." Jake eyed the scuttling soil and the space around him which was full of spyders bouncing up and down on the end of their fine silk ropes. "Makes me dizzy to look at you all though. Question is, I guess, you say you protect the wood, but who for and what are you protecting it from? I hear The General is at work around here."

"Ah-ha, The General." Darius drew his long legs inwards a little. Around him the silk ropes trembled. "The thing is, we have had to play a bit of a funny game with The General. He thinks we're working for him, that we are keeping intruders like your friend there out of his land."

"Well you've done quite good job there," Jake looked up at Maverico, who was still hanging suspended in mid-air. Maverico let out another loud screech.

"I tell you, I am not ze cat burglar. My friend and Princess 'ere will tell you. We are ze muscateers. Descend me now!"

Jake ignored his friend's howls. "But if you're not working for The General, who are you working for?"

"Indeed," said Beatrice, whose ugly markings had rearranged themselves into suitably royal beauty for the occasion. "After all the Wildwoods are mine to inherit."

"Ah, now I see you truly," Darius stepped back in admiration. There were tiny gasps of appreciation from hundreds of points within the silk curtains around them. Beatrice acknowledged them with a royal smile.

"The thing is, we are working, as you might say, like double agents," Darius explained. "It is King Leon whom we serve – or it was. But before he left he gave us a very specific instruction. He said we were to watch over the Wildwoods and particularly to watch out for the Princess.

"He said it was most important for the Princess that we all stuck together. Bit of an odd phrase, I thought."

"Well, ol' Rico's stuck together good an' proper," said Jake. "Do you think you can get him down and undo him?"

CHAPTER 20
TIME TO UNWIND

To capture Maverico took an instant. To lower him to the ground was an altogether different matter. With guidance from Darius and his creative director, a fierce-looking red and black striped character known as Sergeant Pepper, the spyders created a pulley system with one group playing out the thread and another slowly drawing it in. They scuttled every which way, up and down and side to side, winding and unwinding their skeins through the branches. Sergeant Pepper barked his commands in a voice that was a little lower in pitch than Darius's and ever so slightly hoarse.

"Altogether now and PULL! And TWIST! And WIND! And RELEASE!"

On the command "RELEASE" Maverico's bound body began its undignified descent and his wails filled the woodland.

"Aay-yeeee Lento, Lento! Slowly I beseech you! Aaaaah!"

It turned out that Sergeant Pepper's senior web technicians had miscalculated the angles and Maverico's head hit an overhanging branch on the way down. Then his feet got caught up in some ivy. And at the last minute one of the threads hooked itself onto a holly bush and he landed on the ground face first.

Jake smirked. "Least that'll stop his moaning and groaning for a minute."

"Thank you Sergeant. Good job done." Darius looked around him. "Now, I need the sharpest jaws in the wood.

148

We need to get our esteemed guest out of this bondage in one piece."

"ME! ME! ME!" The cries went up from all around as spyders scuttled from every direction.

"Jeepers, they sound like a bunch of wind chimes gone wild," Jake muttered.

For a while Maverico disappeared under a swarm of spyders as they got to work. But in a very short time his yells of protest descended into helpless giggles.

"Ees a-tickling. Oh no! I beg you. Ha! Ha! Ha. Stop!"

Beatrice and Jake were soon giggling as well. The spyders were a bit puzzled at first and then they saw the funny side and began laughing too, until the whole wood shook with laughter and sparkled with silver threads trembling in the sunlight. When Maverico finally managed to stand up, his head was still covered in fine spyder webs which made him look as though he was wearing a baby's bonnet which set them off laughing all over again.

"So, we've got one back," said Jake, when they managed to catch their breath. "Now we've just got to find the others. There's Rufus…"

"And Candy," interrupted Beatrice.

"And Candy, sure thing," Jake looked at her kindly. "And that means The General, of course."

"And zen zere is King Leon!" Maverico added, with a flourish and a bow.

"Can you help us Darius?" Beatrice was not sure whether she was giving an order or asking a favour.

"Delighted to be of service, Your Royal Highness." Darius bounced up and down excitedly on his thread. "But what is this about King Leon? I'm afraid he's long gone."

Around them the spyders nodded their agreement, creating a rather strange wave like effect with all the webs.

"But we saw him, didn't we, Jake? Rico? He was on the train just before ours." Beatrice tried to stop her voice from trembling.

149

"No, no, no!" The tinkling started again as all the spyders chimed in with their leader.

"No, I'm afraid that's impossible my dear. Anything that moves in the wood we know about. Our friend here is evidence of that." Maverico looked shamefaced. "We feel the vibrations, you see."

"So you know where Candy is?" Jake was eager to change the subject. "And what's happened to Rufus?"

Darius cleared his throat. "Well, yes, we knew when Candy arrived back with that Grubsta cat. We could tell there were two of them. At first we thought he must with Gangsta but then we knew something was up because the vibration was far too delicate to be him. Had to be a kitten. Dreadful thing to do."

"So you know where she is?" Beatrice gasped excitedly.

"Not exactly. We tracked her as far as The General's labyrinth. She's in there somewhere. At least, she hasn't come out."

"And Rufus?" Jake's voice was tense.

"Hmm, now, was that the big ginger one? Posh. Fancied himself a bit?"

Beatrice was about to shake her head but Jake nodded. "That's him."

Darius looked troubled. "Well, he was here. We counted him in with you three. He was on the deer track over there. But he's not there now. And I, for one can't feel a thing."

He looked round hopefully at the huge spyder army around him but there was no response.

"Which means?" Jake was getting impatient.

"I wish I knew."

Darius shook his head. All around him the other spyders did the same. The tinkling sounded again. But this time it sounded forlorn, not joyous. Like a great sigh.

CHAPTER 21
INTO THE UNKNOWN

"This is the spot where we last sensed him."

Darius, Sergeant Pepper and the team of senior web technicians were standing with Jake and Beatrice and Maverico on the deer path where Rufus had last been spotted. Beside them was a gaping hole.

"Has he fallen, do you think?" Beatrice was trying to peer down the hole. "It looks like a very long way down."

"Down to where, that's the question." Jake tried to keep the anxiety out of his voice.

The spyders bobbed and weaved in the branches all around but this time the noise they made was more a like a long low continuous hum. It was not a reassuring sound.

"The thing is, he was here. Definitely. But this hole wasn't." Darius scuttled from one end of it to another, just to be absolutely sure. "It happens sometimes round here. Some say it's the effect of the quarrying. Some say different." He hesitated.

"Spit it out, spyder," said Jake. "We ain't got time to mess around."

"No, of course not." Darius sounded a little offended. "The thing is, as I am sure you realise, these woods are alive. They change overnight, sometimes in a second. A hole like this will open up suddenly. And then, just as mysteriously, it will disappear."

"Like a giant mouth closing," said Sergeant Pepper.

Beatrice went cold. She felt her markings sliding down

towards her tail.

Maverico gave a huge howl. "Ze wood, 'e 'as eaten Rufus?"

"Not necessarily." Darius glared at Sergeant Pepper. "We think these tunnels all join up underneath. Rufus could have found a disused entrance to Badger City, for instance. Or a fox lair."

"Not sure that's any better," said Jake gloomily. "The badgers are OK if you approach them right, but foxes? They're a dodgy bunch. And then of course…"

"What Jake?" Beatrice was trying to follow the conversation and control her markings at the same time, which was proving difficult now that she was so upset.

"Well, I s'pose that there hole could lead directly into The General's labyrinth."

For once the spyders were completely still and silent. And so was Maverico. Then Jake spoke again.

"There's nothin' for it. One of us needs to go down there after him." He looked around the group.

"Me, I'll go!" said Beatrice. "Just give me a minute to get sorted." She was trying to persuade her markings to move back into place from where they were hiding in her tail area. It was hard work, like dragging on a very heavy, very reluctant coat.

"No way Bee!" Jake was emphatic. "You are the one we are supposed to be protecting, right?" He looked around. The spyders bobbed their assent.

"And Rico, I think maybe you've been through enough lately. I should be the one to go. That's if you think you and the Princess here can manage without me for a while, that is?"

Beatrice felt her belly loosen then tighten. To be here in the Wildwoods without Jake – or Rufus! Her markings began to slide back towards her bottom all over again. Then she felt Jake's eyes on her. They were warm and reassuring and enfolded her like a soft black cape. Suddenly she felt different. Safe. Even brave. She looked at her shoulders. The black markings were indeed wrapped across her back, meeting at her throat in a gentle embrace. OK, so she did look a little odd with a white chest, four gold legs and a gold tail, but it was quite an original arrangement. She recalled her Queenly Attitudes and sat up straight and tall.

"We'll be just fine, won't we Rico? But how are you going to get down there?"

"I guess the same way Rico did just now of course – if you'll be so kind as to lend me your technicians Darius?"

"Why of course, kind sir." Darius looked across at Sergeant Pepper. "I think perhaps we'll need to think about an extra strong weave here." He nodded his head in the direction of Jake's ample girth.

The spyders seemed very excited as they got to work, spinning and weaving. They made an extra-strong harness for Jake and wound it underneath his belly. Then they attached their strongest 12-ply threads to a nearby oak tree. It was only as Sergeant Pepper announced the start of the lowering process that Beatrice thought of something.

"How's he going to get out of that at the other end?"

The spyders bobbed in consternation. Then Sergeant Pepper spoke.

"Nothing for it. I'll go down with him. I'll be able to help get him free." The Wildwoods vibrated with humming and pinging and the shaking of threads as the spyders considered this option.

"It does seem to be the only way," said Darius, after a while.

Jake turned to Sergeant Pepper. "That's awful kind of you, sir. And I'd sure be glad of the company."

Sergeant Pepper raised one of his legs aloft in a spyder salute.

"Well, if we're going, you'd better jump up." Jake was trying to sound jovial, but Beatrice could feel the tension in his voice.

153

Sergeant Pepper scuttled up Jake's thick black tail and along his spine, finally taking position on top of Jake's head where his red striped body looked like a large blood blister.

"From here I can always escape and hide inside the ears if it becomes necessary," he explained.

"Makes a change from fleas, I suppose," said Jake, still doing his best to sound light-hearted.

"One of the first rules of espionage," said Sergeant Pepper. "Always have an escape route planned." Beatrice thought he was beginning to sound a bit like Rufus.

"Alright for you Sarge." Jake felt the spyder sitting on his head bristle at the familiar address. "But what about my escape route?" He laughed as though he was joking. Beatrice knew better.

With everything in place, the spyders began the delicate task of lowering their charges down into the darkness. Unlike the previous operation, this one took place in almost complete silence. Beatrice sat with Maverico and watched Jake's large, familiar form as it slowly disappeared from view – first the feet, then the belly, then the back, till all that was left was the tip of the tail and the head with its bright red spot. Finally, those too were gone.

Beatrice had never felt so alone. The Autumn night was drawing in and the air was turning cold. Where was Rufus? And where was Jake now? Were they safe? Was she? She felt the black, furry markings wrap themselves around her more tightly, as though they were trying to offer comfort. But a chill still gripped her. Without Jake and without Rufus it was as though half of her own soul was missing.

CHAPTER 22
CONTEMPLATING UGLINESS

"Rico?"

"What Piccolina?"

Maverico was sleeping with one long leg draped across Beatrice. It was actually quite uncomfortable but she knew he was trying to make up to her for Jake's absence, so she didn't complain. Around them the spyders were sleeping off their hard work of the day before.

"We need to talk about Candy."

"Very good my little Princess." Maverico's voice was sleepy. He shifted slightly and closed his eyes again with a sigh.

"No, really Rico. We can't just leave Roof and Jake to do it all. And we can't abandon Candy either. We have to do something to rescue her."

"Maybe you're right, Princess, but for today I think we 'ave done enough."

Seconds later there was a loud snore. Beatrice struggled out from underneath him in disgust. If he was not going to do anything, she certainly was. Candy was not just a friend, she was a loyal subject, which meant Beatrice had a Royal Duty to protect her. She remembered the long hours of training with Sheba – all those lessons on Queenly Attitudes and Contemplating Beauty. What use were they now, to her or to Candy? It would not be long before The General and his lackeys realised their mistake and came looking for the true Princess. She had to do something fast. She needed to disguise herself. But it must be a perfect disguise. One that would keep her safe and allow her to penetrate into the very heart of The General's labyrinth.

She thought about Gangsta and Grubsta and how dirty and smelly they were. The stink that came from the Bad Cats wasn't just mud and filth that could be sorted out with a good wash. It emanated from somewhere deep inside them, from their hearts and minds. They breathed in good clean woodland air and breathed out a foetid stench that poisoned the atmosphere all around them. She puzzled for a while. And then it came to her. Like all the best ideas it was simple, yet obvious. Why hadn't she thought of it before?

Treading as lightly as she could to avoid disturbing the spyders, Beatrice crept off into the woodland. It took her a while to find the place she was looking for but eventually she came across the ideal site. In the far corner of the wood was an unofficial rubbish dump. It was dirty and neglected, piled with old plastic carrier bags and smelling heavily of rotting food and maggots. There were even a couple of empty bottles of lager and some old bottle tops. Beatrice looked at them disdainfully. How could she ever have enjoyed playing silly games?

She knew better now. She knew life was not a game. It could be exciting and fun, but it could also be cruel and horrid. And that was what she would have to become if she was going to stand any chance of succeeding in her mission. A grass snake slithered past, startling her. She thought back to Cedric the sea-serpent and how easily Jake had been able to manipulate and control him with music. Just for a moment she remembered sliding down Cedric's long neck and the joy she had felt leaping along his curved back, but then she stopped herself. This was not a time for fun. Now it was her turn to take control.

Her Royal Highness Princess Beatrice settled down in the middle of the stinking junk heap and put her feet together neatly, on top of a particularly offensive pile of fox poo. A wave of disgust and nausea washed through her. Good. Now she was getting somewhere. Her stomach heaved but there could be no turning back now. Alone, in the filthiest and darkest corner of the Wildwoods, wrapped round with her black cape and her golden tail, Beatrice began the process of Contemplating Ugliness.

She started by thinking back to every sad or difficult moment in her short life. She remembered her mother's constant criticisms. Not just the verbal ones, but the looks, the sighs and the silences, which said so much more. Over and over, she replayed in her head the rejections, the hurts, the times when Sheba had simply turned her head away and refused even to look at her. Beatrice remembered how ugly and worthless she had felt then. She thought about the way her mother had betrayed her with Candy. How Sheba had accused her of lying about Jake's visit. At the thought of Jake, Beatrice momentarily felt herself soften, but she checked the impulse. She needed to be hard both inside and out.

Jake, who was he anyway? A big, fat, lazy good-for-nothing who had never done anything with his life and who chose to fawn over her because she was the Princess and he thought he would get something out of it. Anyway, he had gone now, with some grand gesture which was meant to impress her. As if. And as for that effete ginger tosspot that called himself Rufus – supposed to be a spy but so stupid he couldn't even stop himself falling down a hole as big as a badger – well, good riddance to them both. They must be pretty stupid anyway to care about her. Not to mention that sleeping circus clown that called himself Maverico – quite ridiculous. Beatrice's mind filled with an image of Maverico hanging helpless from the treetops in the spyder's noose and her mouth began to twitch in a smile but she caught herself just in time and turned it to a sneer.

After a long period of focused concentration Beatrice began to think she had made a mistake. Her excitement turned to impatience and then to anger – anger with herself and her own stupidity. It was not working. Her mother was right. She really was a lost cause. She could not even do this one thing right. Not even for her friend who was in mortal danger. She wasn't even good at being bad. Completely useless.

Then she felt the tiniest movement. At last! The lovely, warm, black cape was beginning to slide off her shoulders. It was a horrible feeling. Exposed and vulnerable – a bit like when she had become invisible. Only this time she did not have her friends about her to keep her safe. For a few seconds the fear nearly overwhelmed her, but then she steeled herself again. This was never going to be easy. She had to let go.

After a few minutes she knew it was definitely working. The markings were moving. There was a nasty, crawling sensation in the region of her back and her belly, as though a thousand spyders were trying to swarm over her all at once. It even felt like some of them had got inside her skin and were burrowing into her organs. But, unlike the friendly spyders, these creatures did not tickle. They nipped and stung. Her own markings were turning against her. Beatrice felt sick with pain and disgust, but weirdly satisfied at the same time. This was the only way. She focused once again on the darkness within.

When she had summoned up every worthless and loveless thought she could muster, Beatrice took the final step. She turned all the hatred and revulsion back on herself. The horror of it made her gasp. It was like ice and fire together, hooks and arrows, the deepest despair and the worst loneliness she could ever have imagined. Like looking down the dark hole where Jake and Rufus had gone and knowing it would never, ever end and she would fall forever. And keep on falling. She breathed in darkness till she was suffocating with it.

And then, all at once, the writhing and wriggling stopped. She took a deep breath and opened her eyes. It felt strange because her face had twisted itself into a vile grimace which made opening her eyes difficult. For a while she could not even see straight. And then she stared in amazement.

How had they done it, those markings? How had *she* done it? Made herself so dirty and smelly and ugly and vile? Her legs were bandy and crooked. Her tail was a mixture of zig-zags and spots and triangles but at least it had shapes, un-like her body. Beatrice looked at it and shivered. There were no words to describe the pattern because there was no pat-tern – not even blobs or splodges, just a weird, dark, stinking shapelessness, like the darkness she had felt herself falling through. In some places she was so dark that she disappeared completely into the night. One thing was sure, no one would recognise her now.

CHAPTER 23

THE DARK SIDE

"I say, well done, Your Highness! Perfectly vile."

Beatrice looked round in alarm. Darius was sitting on the branch of an overhanging tree.

"Why thank you, Darius." Beatrice felt her ugly mask begin to crack into a smile. That was no good at all.

"But, Darius, how did you know it was me? I thought I'd done everything right. Or everything wrong, that was the idea. But maybe I was wrong all along. Or right." This good and bad thing was confusing – a bit like Time all over again.

"Aaah, well I'm afraid I felt you leave. I volunteered for the night shift tonight. Give the others a break, you know. And so I followed you, to see what you were up to. Very impressive, I must say."

"Not so impressive if it all dissolves the moment I see a friendly face," sighed Beatrice, watching her belly beginning to transform again.

"Ah well, now I might have a solution for you there." Darius swung down from his branch and stood in front of her. "It was those words of King Leon you see. About us sticking together. It got me thinking."

"I have no idea what you are talking about, Darius." Beatrice's impatience at least stopped her markings from transforming too much for the better.

"Well, I think I know what you are up to," Darius laughed conspiratorially, "and Jake would probably kill me for helping you but I thought a hair net might help. A fur net, I suppose in your case. A bit of skilled web design might just keep those markings in place for you. You saw what we did for your friend Maverico after all. Only it might help with the disguise…if that's what you are after, that is."

"Darius, you're an angel." Beatrice was just about to put her tongue out to give him a big salty lick when she realised her happiness was affecting her markings again and she was in danger of turning back into a Good Cat. She checked herself.

"That's a really stupid idea. Just what I'd expect from a silly spyder that can't keep his webs in order," she snapped, and was gratified to feel her markings return to their ugly mood.

"That's my girl." Darius bobbed his encouragement.

"Don't you 'my girl' me."

"Now then, there's no need to overdo it, dear."

"And don't you dare patronise me either!"

But Darius had taken advantage of the exchange to leap onto her nose and begin spinning. As he worked, the insults continued to fly out of Beatrice's mouth with an alacrity that amazed her.

"That's useless! You've missed a bit!"

"Don't tell me how to do my job."

"Those people who hated you were right all along. You're a stupid, eight-legged ugly monster!"

"That's rich coming from someone covered in filthy fur."

"At least I haven't got a million horrid hairy legs."

"That's it, you can stop now, we're finished." Darius stepped back to admire his work. "Perfect!"

But Beatrice was not giving up so easily. "How arrogant can you be? You're nothing but a vassal, remember? I'll decide what's perfect."

"No it's alright, Your Highness. It's finished. Those markings won't move now. You can be nice again."

"Don't you tell me to be nice, or it will be off with your

head. Or maybe off with your legs. Given the ridiculous lay-out of your body, I suspect it amounts to the same thing."

Darius tutted ostentatiously and scuttled away as fast as his eight legs would carry him. Under cover of darkness Beatrice watched him go and tried to smile but under her new spy-dernet her face remained contorted in a twisted sneer. She spat after him instead. It felt surprisingly satisfying. His plan had worked. There was no going back now.

* * *

Alone in the wood, Beatrice thought about how horrid she had been to Darius. She had never spoken like that to any-one before. Where had it all come from? Darius was a friend and he was trying to help her. She knew that, yet she had not been able to stop herself from behaving badly, even at the end when the fur net he had created was holding her markings firmly in place and she could have been nice again.

Or could she? Once again her mouth twitched at the cor-ners as she remembered his ridiculous legs scuttling away. But just as she began to laugh, pins and needles shot through her body. She grimaced in pain which for some reason made her feel better. Then she realised what must be happening. Of course, the grimace was part of her Bad Cat expression which Darius's web was intended to keep in place. Beatrice was about to smile with relief at this realisation, but before the muscles of her mouth could even move the attack started again. This time is was sharper and deeper, like nails being driven into her flesh and bones and she doubled over onto the filthy rubbish tip. Then, just as quickly as it had begun, the pain subsided. Beatrice had the distinct impression that she was being threatened. But by what or by whom? Was it something to do with Darius's spydernet? Or did it spring from a deeper power? Beatrice's mouth drooped in genuine misery as she realised something alarming. The character that she had created as a disguise might actually have a mind of its own.

* * *

All around her the trees were beginning to light up with the morning sun. She remembered how beautiful they had seemed in their autumn splendour. But now, as she looked at them, she could not feel anything at all. What on earth could be special about a few dying trees? She tried to recall that past pleasure but it was like trying to walk with a limb that had been cut off. For the first time Beatrice thought she understood how The General must feel.

She tried jumping up and down in the fallen leaves but even though her legs moved they felt as heavy as her heart did. And the noise the dead leaves made was not a friendly, crunchy sound. This morning they crackled belligerently and when she pounced on them they were full of briars which prickled and cut into her paws. The pain took up all the space inside her head, until there was no room for anything else and she felt that the old Beatrice had gone for good and what remained must be ugly and bad through and through, inside and out.

"Good riddance to 'er I say! Better off without 'er, snobby little snitch!" The strange sharp voice inside her head was the same one that had been so insulting to Darius. It spoke in a peculiar accent that Beatrice did not recognise.

She closed her eyes and thought back to her travels with the muscateers – how there had been no difference between millions of years ago and a hundred years ago and yesterday. They were all true but because they happened one after the other you could never see the whole story at once. That was what Time was for. Maybe only Time would tell if she was good or bad. Or whether she could be both at once. And then she thought about weird Mr Schrödinger and his secret cat

163

that was both alive and dead until somebody found her and decided which she was.

So who was Beatrice when she was all alone and no one was watching except herself? Who was looking at her now? And who was looking at the other creature, the Bad Cat, inside her? If she did not look at it or listen to it, was it dead? Or alive?

In any case, Beatrice decided, she would not find out who was watching her by sitting around with her eyes closed. She needed to take a good look, and then, like Mr Schrödinger, she would know for certain. She took a deep breath and opened her eyes. But what she saw was not what she was expecting.

The world had disappeared.

CHAPTER 24
THE BRIGHT SIDE

Where previously the woods had been filled with the silvery light of dawn, now there was just a milky whiteness. Beatrice could still breathe easily but she couldn't see anything beyond her own paws which appeared and disappeared like strange, magical creatures that did not belong to her. In some places the whiteness was so thick she thought it must be a solid wall but when she took a step it allowed her through anyway. The ground was firm beneath her paws. Yes the world was still there, it was just invisible. Or maybe it had changed its markings. She took another step. And another one. With each one a little of the woods revealed themselves and a little more vanished.

In places she could see the shapes of the tree trunks looming above. Except they did not look like tree trunks. They were more like an army of giants lying in wait for her. She turned slightly to her left and tripped over a giant sea-serpent.

"Hello Cedric!" she said, delightedly. But it turned out the wavy creature was nothing more than a dead branch lying on the ground. Somehow this made the woods seem more dangerous rather than less so. Beatrice decided the best way of avoiding monsters would be to climb up one of the giant trees.

It was not easy to pick the right tree when all she could see was its bottom parts, but she chose one with nice thick, wide roots and ridged bark which she could get her claws into easily. She climbed almost straight up, like a koala bear, until she reached a low, fat branch and had a rest. Just as she was wondering where to go next, another branch appeared above her. And then another. On she went, climbing higher and higher, passing sleeping blue tits and busy blackbirds and chattering chaffinches, until suddenly the white stuff had disappeared and she felt the sun, warm on her poor, ugly markings. The shock of seeing them properly again made her feel sick and ashamed.

It was only when she looked down at last that she realised what had happened. The world had not disappeared. It was just that part of the sky had fallen down. Not the bright blue part, which was surprisingly empty and clear close up, but the white clouds that floated in it. From up here she could see them clearly. They lay spread out on the ground below like strips of cotton wool with the trees poking their heads out of the top. Beatrice sighed. It was a very confusing day.

∗ ∗ ∗

"Lovely, innit?"

Beatrice looked round in surprise to find a large scruffy jackdaw sitting next to her.

"You think so?" she replied frostily, surprised at how grumpy she sounded, then realised it must be the Bad Cat speaking. "The sky's fallen in and you think that's pretty? I'd say it's disastrous." Her tone became petulant, then patronising. "What if the sun does the same thing? And the moon? And the stars? Not so lovely then, I'd say."

"Ha ha ha ha ha!" The jackdaw threw his head back gleefully. "Nice one, puss. Never 'eard no one describe fog like that before. Ha ha ha!" He wiped his beak on the tree bark. "Still, s'pose it's true in a way. Them clouds ain't fallen nowhere, they're just having a low day. You know the sort? I'm sure your do." His eyes glittered with impertinence.

166

"But they'll lift soon enough. The sun'll melt them away and then there'll be no more mystery. It'll be same old, same old. You'll see, underneath all that." He cocked his head to one side and thought for a moment. "Bit like you really."

"Watch your mouth or I'll have you for breakfast!" Good Cat or Bad Cat, Beatrice was not standing for this.

"But that's just it, innit?" The jackdaw paused to peck at an insect. "You won't. I mean, you might look like one of The General's lot but you and me, we wouldn't be sitting 'ere chatting if that was so. You'd have tried to kill me by now. Not that you'd have managed it of course. I'm very quick on the wing."

Beatrice thought that she must be a truly Bad Cat after all because now she dearly wanted to leap on him and shake him till his feathers flew.

The jackdaw shook his head. "It don't make sense." He thought for a moment. "You 'idin' from someone?"

"Certainly not," said Beatrice indignantly. "I'm just in disguise, that's all."

"Heh, heh, heh!" The jackdaw started cackling again. "Well, let me tell you luv, you'll need to do better than that. Not that I know who you are of course. Jus' I know you're not one of them…

"No, don't tell me. It's more fun guessing. Adds a bit of spice, like. Course I don't mind telling you who I am. The name's Jack, though you've probably guessed that by now. Jack Daw. No mystery there, puss. Heh, heh heh!"

Beatrice was speechless with rage. It took her rather by surprise because it was unlike anything she had felt before. This rage was different to just feeling cross. Emotion streamed through her body with the power of the wind and the ice and the baking suns all together. She tried to push it down and away but it built up inside her until it was so powerful that it forced her jaws open and came out of her like a wild animal.

The noise it made was neither a hiss nor a yowl, nor even a screech, but a huge, deep roar. The trees around shook with the force of it and their branches waved wildly. It blew Jack right off his perch and he was left flapping around in mid-air. The sound was so alien that Beatrice looked around in alarm to see what terrifying creature had made it. Then she realised it was her. Or the strange Bad Cat within her.

"Ha, ha, ha!" Jack was waving his wings up and down enthusiastically. "That's more like it luv. Even 'ad me fooled for a minute." He landed back on the branch and looked at her more closely. "Whoever you are darlin', you're something special. Oh, now don't take on so, you should be proud."

To Beatrice's embarrassment and shame, huge tears were sliding uncontrollably down her ugly face.

"I…I'm so sorry, Mr Jack. I mean Mr Daw." Beatrice could not believe she was actually apologising to a bird. But she missed her muscateers so much and there was something about Jack that reminded her of Jake – and not just the name. It was the cheek and the attitude and the kindness. How could anyone be kind to someone who looked so ugly? And who was so horrible too.

"It's just that I don't know who I am or who I'm meant to be. I had this idea, you see, to disguise myself as a Bad Cat to rescue my friend from The General, but, like you say, I'm no good at it. I'm even no good at being no good. And now I've got this monster inside that I can't control. It makes me think horrid thoughts and it even speaks for me, sometimes. Well, you heard it." The tears started to flow again.

"Not at all, luv. You're just a bit mixed up, I'd say. Problem is, you're taking this thing all too seriously. Think of it more like a game, play-acting. Gettin' one over on 'imself and 'is mates." Jack side-stepped along the branch and looked at her hard with his head on one side.

"You need to think about the eyes, though, luv."

"Eyes?" Beatrice blinked through her tears.

"Yes, they're a dead giveaway. Didn't your mother teach you that cat trick? Like 'idin' your real self behind those eyes. Make 'em like windows, only they got to be one-way glass."

"Oh, you mean Queenly Attitudes," said Beatrice, and then checked herself. She must not give away her royal identity.

"Dunno about that, luv. Just keep a bit back, that's all. Like 'ide and seek. Only don't let them find you.

"An' while we're about it, make the most of that nasty side. Nothin' wrong with it in the right place. It can protect you, warn you about dangers the nice side of you couldn't even imagine. A bit of ugliness now an' then never 'urt no one, I say."

Beatrice was not sure she understood what Jack Daw was talking about. And she was finding his over-familiarity irritating. But maybe that was the Bad Cat being bad-tempered and not her true self. It was hard to tell. She did like his idea of a game, though.

She remembered all the times she had played in the attic with Jake and Candy and felt comforted. She was good at games. Then she thought about the long, boring lessons in Queenly Attitudes and Contemplating Beauty. Maybe they had been worthwhile too. Maybe Sheba knew more than she had been letting on.

"Thank you Jack."

"No problem, luv." Jack ruffled his feathers in a nonchalant way.

"And Jack? If you see my friends – they're called Jake and Rufus and Rico – will you explain, you know, in case they don't recognise me?"

Jack eyed her beadily. "I don't think you need to worry luv. And don't forget, with a roar like that you can do anything. But probably best just keep it inside with the rest of you for now. Don't want to alert the enemy, do we?

"Now, all the best to you my luv, but I've got an urgent

appointment with a murmuration of starlings at the other side of the wood. Must fly. Ha, ha, ha!"

"Goodbye, I hope we meet again." Beatrice watched his gawky shape turn into graceful flight and wished she could fly too. She looked down and was relieved to see the clouds were lifting and going back up into the sky. Maybe they had just been playing hide and seek too, with the woods. Anyhow they would soon be back where they belonged. If only she could be too.

She thought of Jake's gentle eyes and how her own black fur had wound itself round her like a shawl when he looked at her. Did he know about Queenly Attitudes? Was that secret gaze just for her, or could anybody see it? Jake seemed incapable of hiding anything.

Was he safe? She tried to warm her heart up by thinking about him. But today there was no lovely black shawl to keep her cosy. Her Bad Cat markings stayed stubbornly in place. She should be pleased – Darius had done a good job. But what if she never found Candy, or Jake and the others again? Would she stay like this forever?

CHAPTER 25
CALL OF THE WILD

The sun was bending its head towards the far hilltops. The two were nearly touching. Beatrice could just make them out through the thinning leaves. She seemed to have been wandering now for hours, looking for The General or his labyrinth – though since she did not know what a labyrinth was she did not know how she would tell if she found it anyway.

Jake had told her it was a sort of tunnel which went round and round so you got lost, which sounded a lot like what she and the muscateers had been doing ever since they left the attic. Maybe the whole of the Wildwoods was actually a labyrinth because she really did not know where she was going, or for that matter where she had been. Jack had told her that when the fog lifted it would be *same old, same old* but Beatrice had not really known where she was before so that did not help. Certainly, it all looked the same. There were just trees everywhere and muddy paths that all looked alike, if you could find them under the leaves.

She felt lost and alone and foolish and stupid. Foolish for having thought she could rescue Candy on her own and stupid for not being able to find her way around what would, after all, be her very own Queendom one day. Then she wondered if those feelings really belonged to her or to the Bad Cat inside. The one with the ugly markings who hated everything and everyone. Perhaps it was the Bad Cat who was the stupid one. If she were only left to herself Beatrice would be clever and confident and would know the right path to take. But if that were true why on earth had clever Beatrice created the stupid creature and why had she allowed Darius to weave the web that held them prisoner together? Her philosophical ruminations were interrupted by a scuffling behind her. Something was disturbing the autumn leaves.

She crouched on her belly behind a large tree trunk which hid her from view and waited. A big buck rabbit raced past, its white tail bobbing behind. Stupid arrangement, that. Beatrice's markings bristled under their spyder net. What use was a bobbing white ball? You could not wave it if you were happy or angry. It could not help you balance. All it did was show everyone you were scared and running away, so whatever was chasing you could see you more easily. Another rabbit passed her, a slightly smaller one this time. Then another and another. Something was frightening them badly.

Beatrice's curiosity got the better of her and she stepped out from her hiding place. She sniffed the air, pricked her ears and listened hard. She could hear a faint gasping, snivelling sound from somewhere nearby. Slowly she padded forward. Yes, there it was – a tiny baby rabbit, all alone and paralysed by fear. The only sign of life was its nose which twitched and drizzled pathetically.

The Bad Cat leapt in Beatrice's empty belly and she felt herself overwhelmed by the urge to take the cute baby bunny in her jaws and break its neck. It would make a delicious evening meal and she was hungry, after all. But the very ferocity of the desire that ran through her shocked Beatrice and she realised she was in danger of losing control altogether.

She took a moment to practise her Attitudes, to recall the Queen somewhere within – that mythical creation of Sheba's who remained always calm, safe and serene, undistracted by the storm of emotions and events. Then she remembered Jake's tale about King Leon and how, since his disappearance,

The General had refused to comply with the rabbit quota system and was killing everything in sight so that soon there would be no rabbits left at all. She looked at the tiny, terrified creature in front of her and despite her angry markings and her wild hunger, not to mention the wild cat that raged inside her, she felt sorry for it. And there was also the important question of loyalty to the absent King Leon.

"All right, all right," she muttered grumpily, "let's get you somewhere safe."

The baby rabbit did not reply. It just trembled from its ludicrously large ears to its ridiculous tail. Beatrice stretched out and took it in her mouth, fighting back the urge to bite down hard. The silly animal began to squeal.

"Hush," she tried to say, but her mouth was full of rabbit fur so no sound came out. She carried it back to her own hiding place and laid it gently between two big tree roots. Once on the earth it did not move, but at least it stopped squeaking. Beatrice kicked over the dead leaves until the baby rabbit was nearly covered.

"There, that's better," she said, as much to herself as to the rabbit, who appeared to be in some sort of trance. "You stay there. I'm just going to see if I can find your parents. Don't move."

It was a rather unnecessary instruction since the little fellow appeared to be quite incapable of moving anywhere. Beatrice set off after the other rabbits. Her own fear seemed to have quite dissolved in the task of looking after someone else. She ran fast because the rabbits had had quite a start on her. She was just beginning to enjoy her own speed and the sense of freedom that came with it, when she tripped over something on the ground. She thought it must be a tree root or a broken branch, but then something grabbed her from behind and she heard a familiar, unpleasant laugh.

"Well, well! Who have we here?"

She did not have to look round to know the voice belonged to Gangsta.

"Runnin' away from someone, are we?"

Gangsta stood over her, his paws on either side of her shoulders and his scrawny face pushed into hers. His breath smelt like rancid rat.

"Dunno where you think you're going darlin'. But nothin' moves in these woods without my say so. Mine and The General's, that is."

For a moment Beatrice's mind went completely blank. Nobody had ever attacked her before. There had been plenty of play fights, of course, but this was for real. She looked up at Gangsta's yellow fangs, noting that one of them was broken off at the tip. Then she spotted his missing whiskers and remembered how Rufus had trapped them in his guitar and how Maverico had played them like a violin and she fought the urge to giggle.

She heard Jack Daw's voice in her head. *Keep a bit back. Think of it like play-acting.* This fight might be real in Gangsta's eyes but what he did not know was that she was not real. At least, what he saw was not real. He thought he was dealing with a commoner, albeit an uncommonly hideous one. But the real Beatrice was hidden, deep inside and was not to be defined by mere markings. She was wrapped round in her ugliness. It felt creepy, dirty, angry and remarkably safe, a bit like she was wearing armour. She was just wondering how to reply to Gangsta when, to her amazement, the ugliness began to speak of its own accord.

"Think I don't know that?"

The voice was sharp, like the one she had heard earlier inside her head. It was also considerably deeper than her own and a little hoarse. And it spoke with that peculiar accent which Sheba would definitely have defined as vulgar.

"I was just running to get away from those foxes," the voice continued. "They're quite out of control. The General wants to have a word with them if you ask me. Great huge stinking things."

She felt Gangsta flex his claws on her belly.

"It's not for the likes of you to say what The General should or shouldn't do. Look at you. Yuck!" Gangsta stepped back and a drool of spittle dropped from his jaws onto Beatrice's face. She would have grimaced, but her markings were already fixed in their mask of disgust and scorn so there was no need.

"'Ow come you know about The General anyway? Just where have you come from? Ain't seen the likes of you round 'ere before."

Where had she come from? If only Beatrice knew.

"That's cos I ain't been round 'ere," the stranger inside her replied confidently. "Been in the city."

Gangsta's undamaged ear pricked up at this. The other one remained hanging dismally down.

"The city eh? What's an ugly little thing like you doin' there?"

The new Beatrice or, rather, the Bad Cat inside apparently received this remark as a compliment.

"Why thank you kind sir. Not as ugly as you, of course." She watched Gangsta preen himself with pleasure at her words then spat hard at him to show she was no soft touch before continuing.

"Born there, wasn't I? On the streets. Never knew no different." The words were flowing as though they had a life of their own, which perhaps they did. Beatrice settled back inside herself and waited with Gangsta to hear the rest of the story.

"Lost me Mam when I was a few weeks old. After that I lived on takeaways mainly. The odd rat if it wasn't too big. Used to raid the cat flaps occasionally, take the food left for those soft, flabby spoilt things. Disgusting. What do they call themselves? 'Ouse cats?" She spat the words out of her mouth. Beatrice watched Gangsta flinch in sympathy.

175

"Any'ow," the voice continued, "I was managin' fine until this tabby cat appeared. Big, powerful thing. Name of Leon."

At the sound of the name, Gangsta leapt back from her. His single black eye gleamed warily.

"Leon!" He shook his head. "You've seen him?"

Beatrice took advantage of the moment to roll over and set herself upright once more.

"Obviously not since I left. But, yes, I have." The voice paused for dramatic effect.

"'E changed everything. I mean, me and my mates, we'd got the streets sewn up, you know? Like you 'ave 'ere in the woods. But this guy comes in and says it's all a disgrace and starts orderin' us around, just like 'e owns the place. Gets these street patrols goin'. Talks about what 'e calls *the importance of personal cleanliness*." Just for a moment the voice took on the accent and tone of Sheba at her most imperious, then it changed back again.

"'E said we had to make sure that there was enough food for everyone. I mean, who's 'e tryin' to kid? Got to fight for yourself, I say. 'E actually started negotiating with the 'ouse cats, can you imagine? Said we shouldn't be stealin'. 'E even got some of 'em to agree to donate. Offer an open house, like, maybe one day a week?"

"And you let him?" Gangsta's face was a picture of horror. Beatrice was beginning to enjoy herself – or her other self. This Bad Cat she had conjured up was not so stupid after all. She added a good scratch for extra impact.

"Never, course not. Me, I'd never give in. But the others – one by one 'e bought them off. The streets became safe. Life weren't no fun anymore. No edge. No risk. Not even hunger. My gang, they just got fat and lazy. That's what an easy life does.

"But me? I'm wild through and through, I guess. I did my bit for a while. Messed up the street patrol rotas. Stole the

176

newborn kittens and dumped them way down on the estate where they'd have to learn the proper way to survive. But, well, no one fought back. It wasn't no fun being bad on my own."

"You want fun?" said Gangsta. His haunches were up now and his tail was lashing. "Being bad ain't supposed to be fun. How do I know Leon himself hasn't sent you, since you seem to know him so well?"

Beatrice would have hesitated but her other self appeared unfazed by the interrogation. "Thing is," it continued, "no one has seen Leon for weeks. We thought he might be dead, but then I did hear he used to run this place – in the days before The General, that is – and I thought maybe he'd come back.

"If that's so, then, well, I need a good fight. I haven't had one for months. And so if he has come 'ere, I'd like to offer my services to you. 'E destroyed my world and I'd like to pay 'im back, see."

"And if he's not here?" Gangsta paced around her suspiciously.

"Well, if he's not, I'd still rather be here with you than there. A girl needs a change sometimes. Call of the wild and all that, you know."

"Hmmm. We'll see what The General says."

Gangsta swiped her hard across the head. His sharp claws cut into her skull. She saw the blood dripping down onto the earth and the smell of it woke an energy within her. She threw herself at him as hard as she could, knocking him completely off his paws, and sank her strong young teeth into his bony old back. He yowled with pain. Something inside Beatrice thrilled with delight. She bit him again and again, enjoying the surge of power and cruelty and the taste of his blood, salty and warm in her mouth. Who would have thought being bad could be so exciting? Maybe this new creature knew a thing or two after all.

The next moment she felt jaws tightening around her own neck from behind. She wrestled her head around to see the huge, stinking animal which had hold of her. It was Grubsta, the one who had kidnapped Candy. Bigger and meaner than Gangsta and altogether more filthy.

Even without looking, Beatrice would have known who it was. The stench was overwhelming. Mud and manure. Stale fish. Sour milk. Rotting teeth. Putrid flesh. The stink of his breath caused her belly to heave as he picked her up and shook her from side to side like a dead rat.

Once upon a time her markings would have flinched and shrunk from him – probably even tried to run away. And Beatrice would have had to follow them, like a coward, always assuming she could have wriggled free. But once upon a time she was a soft, vulnerable kitten who carried her insides on the outside and knew nothing of the Wildwoods. Once upon a time her markings could move. Now, bound in place by the spydernet, they could not budge an inch even if they wanted to – though she had the distinct impression that the Bad Cat within was enjoying herself far too much to run away anyway.

"They can't see me, they don't know me, they can't hurt me," Beatrice repeated to herself.

"Alright boys, you win. Where are we going?" said the fearless street kitten. Her voice was a bit constricted on account of Grubsta's teeth still digging into her throat. "What's that they say in the stories? Take me to your leader. Let's hope he'll recognise a good fighter when he sees one. Come on! Chop, chop!"

To Beatrice's surprise Gangsta started to laugh. He had clearly recovered from the attack. Even so it was not a nice friendly chuckle like Jake's. It sounded more like a cross between a snort and a cackle and a sneer.

"What d'you think, Grub? She's a wild one right enough. Worth taking 'er back with us to meet The General? Not like that prissy little fake you got your claws into. Now put her down for a minute. Don't think she'll be going nowhere somehow."

Grubsta looked at Gangsta and grunted. He opened his mouth and Beatrice dropped to the ground. He stood over her, his breath foul in her face. But he said nothing.

"Apologies if my friend 'ere is a bit quiet. The General cut 'is tongue out for that mistake, so 'e don't speak no more. Not that 'e ever made much sense before, like. Catflap open, but nobody 'ome, as they say. To mistake that little chambermaid for the Princess. I mean, 'ow could 'e?" Gangsta gave Beatrice a scornful look.

"Not goin' to make that mistake with you, are we, luv? The state of you!" His voice had almost an admiring tone. "Ugliest thing I've seen in years. Still, maybe you'll be able to get something out of, what do they call 'er? Candy? Find out where they're 'idin' 'er."

"Just let me at 'er Gangsta. I'll put 'er in 'er place, right enough." Beatrice's spine was tingling with excitement. The plan was working. Whoever she was, the evil street kitten was doing well.

"'Ow come you know my name?" His voice was sharp with suspicion.

"Oh, but they've all 'eard of you in the city," Beatrice heard herself reply. "The General's right paw. That's what they call you. From what I 'ear he could do with one." She sniggered.

"Enough! You'll speak with respect of The General!" Gangsta flexed his claws menacingly. Then his voice softened. "And what else do they say about me?"

"Oh, well, some say that 'e'd be nothin' without you. And Grubsta of course," she added, aware that the large silent cat behind her was beginning to arch his back dangerously. "But they say Gangsta's the brains and Grubsta's the brawn."

On cue, Grubsta backed his large bulk up against a nearby tree trunk and sprayed forcibly. The stench filled the air so that Beatrice nearly choked.

Gangsta took a deep breath in and smiled so that his broken fangs glittered in the moonlight. "Nice one, Grub. Got to make sure they all know we're 'ere."

"Who's they?" asked the voice, ungrammatically.

"Oh the badgers, I suppose, and the foxes. And that effete lot of felines that fawn around the Princess."

"What felines would those be now?"

"Ask a lot of questions, don't you?" Gangsta eyed her suspiciously. "Don't you worry your 'ead about them. That's for us to know. Grub! Pass me some goose grass. Now shut those weird eyes. They give me the creeps. And this'll keep 'em closed till we get there."

Beatrice shut her eyes, wondering what it was that Gangsta found so creepy about them. She felt the sticky stems of the goose grass wind tightly around her skull and realised what they were doing. Her eyes were stuck fast. They had blindfolded her.

They walked in single file, with Gangsta at the front and Grubsta a silent, smelly presence at the rear. Beatrice went in the middle so that Grubsta could keep an eye on her and make sure she didn't escape. Gangsta could not do that particular job because he only had one eye anyway and he needed it to see where he was going.

She stepped cautiously, afraid of tripping, but when she slowed down too much Grubsta nipped her ankles, so she had to use her nose and her ears instead of her eyes. She listened for the sound of dead leaves rustling in front of her as Gangsta chose his path. If she concentrated hard she could even hear when he sidestepped to avoid a fallen tree or jumped over a rabbit hole and so she could copy him.

Jake had taught Beatrice a bit about woodland fungi and she could identify the separate scents of mushrooms and toadstools and tree fungus they passed. She could tell when they passed the stinky foxes' lair and when they stepped over badger bedding laid out to air. She knew when they reached the edge of the woodland because, along with the tree bark and the moss, she could smell sweet sheep droppings. The grass was soft and wet beneath her paws and even the air felt different – it moved more freely and easily. From the open sky came a repeated mewing sound, a bit like a lost kitten. Could cats fly then, wondered Beatrice? Could The General have acquired wings as well as a false leg?

"See that bird up above?" Gangsta asked, as if sensing her thoughts. "Oh no, I forgot, you can't can you?" There was cruel glee in his voice. "Still, you'll be able to hear it. That there's a buzzard. Great huge bird, big as a badger. That'll have a kitten like you for breakfast. Peck your eyes out first, of course. I should know. That's 'ow I lost mine."

"Oh yeah?" The voice sound unimpressed, despite the fact that Beatrice's legs had turned to jelly. "So if that's true, 'ow come you're not dead then?"

"That's all down to The General," said Gangsta. "'E's the reason I'm still 'ere. 'E came and saved me. Course that was back in Leon's time, before 'e took over the Wildwoods. An' before 'e lost 'is leg 'an all. Long time ago now.

"The General was in charge of the troops then. No one to match 'im, I'm telling you. When 'e saw me in trouble he threw 'imself at that buzzard. 'E got the other cats to pitch in, like. One took 'is tail, I think that was Fatty Jake. And the other two, Rico and Roof, they took a wing each. Grand battle, it was. Not that I was in a position to appreciate it at the time, like.

"But, no doubt about it, The General's a great soldier. Without 'im, I'd have been a buzzard's breakfast, for sure."

Beatrice was relieved when they turned back into the woods once more. She listened to the buzzard's mewings fading into the distance and thought about Gangsta's story. She knew, of course, that Jake and Maverico and Rufus had once fought alongside The General – Jake had told her what a loyal and courageous warrior he had been. Yet somehow this made it much more real. The General had not always been bad. But then neither had she.

CHAPTER 26
LA BELLA DONNA

"Now then, what have we here?" The voice was unfamiliar and would have struck a chill in Beatrice's heart were it not for the fact that she was shivering so much already. The further they had gone into the labyrinth – for that was where they must be, Beatrice had decided – the colder it became. Not the nice, crisp cold that used to wake her up and make her jump and play to keep warm but the damp sort that seeps through even the thickest fur and stiffens the muscles before settling in the bones. Each step had become painful – the more so because of Grubsta's teeth which kept nipping her ankles.

A shame it was only his tongue that was cut out and not his teeth, Beatrice thought. She could not decide if this was a good thought or a bad one since it gave her so much bitter pleasure. Everything was getting rather muddled.

Beatrice was still blindfolded, but she could sense they were in a cave of sorts. The air around her sounded different, like it was hollow. She could hear something dripping in a corner. She hoped it was water, not blood. Yet at the thought of blood she found her mouth watering, which was very confusing. The air smelt of wet stone and stale cat and putrid flesh. She sniffed distastefully. Probably rotten rabbit.

"Ha ha! She's turning her nose up already."

The voice was low and menacing. Chill, like the air. Cold, like stone. Hard, like iron. Beatrice thought back to Jake's

183

story about The General and the iron leg which grew into his soul. Here he was, at last.

"Found 'er in the woods," Gangsta said, with some satisfaction. "Says she comes from the city. Claims to have lived on the streets."

"Well, she's ugly enough for it." The General gave what might have been a chuckle but sounded like metal bars knocking together. "Nobody would take her in would they? Well come on, what are you waiting for? Let's get this blindfold off and have a good look."

Grubsta sprang into action, swiping at her face over and over to dislodge the goosegrass. His claws cut into her eyelids and her sensitive nose but Beatrice fought the urge to yell or retaliate, remembering that she was supposed to be a street cat who had lived through much harder times than this. When at last she could open her eyes she saw that Grubsta had got his paws tangled up in the sticky plant and was walking backwards around the cave in an effort to free himself. He really was stupid. But she was not able to enjoy the spectacle properly because there was so much else to look at.

The floor of the cave was strewn with rabbits' ears, so thick in places they were like a carpet. Feathers or all sizes and colours fanned out against the walls – black and blue and red and yellow. Every fold of rock was full of trophies of one sort or another. Bits of beak were stacked up in places to form towers. A large skull peeped out from behind an outcrop of stone. Rows of glittering eyeballs stared down at her from a ledge above. Two dead crows hung from the centre of the ceiling. Deer pelts and fox tails trailed from other parts of the roof. And there, hunched against a rock in the corner, a bushy fox fur wrapped around his shoulders, was The General, just like Jake had said.

He was an enormous cat with eyes of hard, emerald green and Beatrice could see that he had once been handsome. His face was wide and his shoulders were broad and muscular. Tufts of dirty gold fur sprang from his large ears. He pushed himself upright with some difficulty and Beatrice was reminded of the old metal train with its heavy cargo shuddering into life. His iron leg clanked on the cave floor and she tried not to stare at it as he walked towards her. But then he raised it up and waved it right in her face.

"Street cat eh? What do they call you then?"

Up to this point Beatrice had been so concerned with her new ugly markings that she had not even considered a new name. But the stranger inside was ahead of her.

"Bella," it announced confidently. The General banged his leg into the ground, but whether in amusement or anger it was hard to tell.

"Bella, my peg leg!" he roared. "With a face like that?"

Beatrice forced herself to look directly into his eyes, hoping they would not give her away, as the new voice spoke from inside her.

"Belladonna, Your Excellency. As you know, a most beautiful and efficient poison." She sounded cool and deadly. "But Bella will do for short."

"Poison, indeed?" The General looked suspicious. "And just who are you planning on killing?"

"That depends on who you ask me to kill," she purred menacingly. At no point in her plans had Beatrice considered the possibility of flirting with The General, but she had to admit this Belladonna's tactics seemed to be working. His eyes glittered as he stomped around the room.

"Thing is, sir," Gangsta sidled up to the big cat, "she also says she's seen Leon."

"Who?" The General swung around quickly, waving his iron leg, which hit Beatrice on the side of the head and almost knocked her out.

"Not for some weeks, Excellency," she said hastily. "Like

185

I told Gangsta 'ere, it were Leon that spoiled things for me. That's why I came looking for you."

"And why would you want me?" The General pushed his huge face into hers menacingly. Beatrice forced herself not to pull away.

"Well, why wouldn't I?" Belladonna's harsh voice took on a soft, seductive tone. "Strong, fierce, adventurous…your name is legendary." Beatrice listened in amazement. What would she come out with next?

The General grunted, then walked slowly all the way round her, staring hard and occasionally poking her belly and flanks with his iron foot. When he had come full circle he stood and regarded her for a few minutes before speaking.

"Well," he said at length, "you smell better than that prissy little thing we've got ourselves landed with back there." He jerked his head in the direction of a narrow gap in the stone. "All that lavender and rosewater. Yuck! Maybe…" He stopped for a moment.

"What, Sir?" Gangsta was almost on his knees in deference. Grubsta stayed at the back of the cave, Beatrice noticed. His head and his tail hung low.

"Perhaps she could persuade that Cotton Candy, or whatever she's called, to take us to the real Princess." The General was looking at Gangsta as he spoke, which was a good thing because he did not see Beatrice's ears prick up at the mention of Candy's name. She made her next purr extra low and threatening.

"But my lord…" How did you address a General who thought he was a king, she wondered. Another lesson Sheba had left out. "My lord, why would you want the Princess? After all, you already rule the Wildwoods."

Beatrice – or maybe Belladonna, she could no longer tell which – decided to take a risk. She crouched low to the ground and wiggled her hindquarters provocatively. "And

186

from what I've heard," she continued, "she's an extremely difficult character. Very moody and changeable."

The General eyed her suspiciously. "It's the changeability that's the issue. You wouldn't know, being born in the city, but there was a prophecy. That Princess will have powers no other cat has ever had. We have to find her before she develops them properly. She has to give them up to me, along with the Kingdom. Or else she dies."

"Very good, my Lord," said Belladonna – it was definitely her now, thought Beatrice. A true Princess could never behave like this. "But what could these powers be? I can't imagine anyone whose powers could outshine yours."

"Enough!" The General's leering face became suddenly dark and menacing. "You know what they say about curiosity? It killed the street cat. And don't think I can't keep my threats. Ask Grubsta. Though of course he won't be able to tell you. Ha ha ha!" Beatrice glanced over at poor Grubsta who was now crouching, terrified, in a corner.

"Take her away then." The General jerked his leg imperiously. "She can look after the other one, I suppose."

"Wait a moment, Excellency. I'm not serving no princess – least of all a fake one." Belladonna spat the words out fiercely. Then her tone softened a little. "I've come to serve you my Lord. To fight." She scratched her claws on a nearby deerskin.

"You'll do as The General says," Gangsta growled. "Else you'll pay the price." He licked his lips lasciviously.

"Listen here Belladonna, or whatever you call yourself," The General spoke with disdain, "a street cat like you wouldn't know the first thing about fighting here. Might look like a pretty woodland but, believe me, it's a jungle out there. Still, there is something you might be able to do if you want to stay here – alive, that is." He sniggered. "A chance for you to show us what you're made of.

"I want you to befriend this Candy Pandy, or whatever she calls herself. Find out what she knows. Because she knows something, that's for sure."

"Sort of like an undercover mission then," said Belladonna, nonchalantly. Beatrice's head was spinning. Her plan was working out better than she had hoped. Technically speaking, of course she was already undercover as Belladonna and that was quite enough to deal with. Now she had to add another layer. She hoped she would be able to find her way out from under both of them eventually.

"Don't get above yourself, Bella. Remember, you're just a street cat with a small secret, doing a service." The General spat the words out. Before Beatrice could stop her Belladonna spat back – hard and long. For a moment Beatrice thought the game was up but then she saw The General's face contort into what passed for a smile.

"Spirit! That's what I like to see. Now Grubsta here will take you to your cell and you'll meet your new little friend."

Grubsta got up with a grunt and began nudging her from behind and nipping her ankles again. Belladonna swung round to fight but, to Beatrice's relief, she turned her snarl to a laugh. "You're so funny Grub! Alright, alright, I'm on my way."

He pushed his charge in the direction of some narrow steps cut into the cave wall which Beatrice had not noticed before. A tiny opening at the top led to a narrow passage. Beatrice could get through quite easily but it took Grubsta a while to squeeze his great bulk between the rocks. It would be quite impossible for The General, Beatrice noted, even if he could manage to get up the steps. A few yards further on they came to a fork in the path. Which way? Obviously Grubsta could not tell her and she could not make out a clear direction from his head butts on her rear. She stood still and listened.

In between the drip-drip of water seeping through the

rocks she could hear a faint whimpering sound. Her heart began to race with excitement. Behind her Grubsta panted and grunted. Somewhere in the darkness, Candy was crying.

CHAPTER 27

UNDERCOVER

"What's all that racket about? Dear, dear, I never 'eard the like!"

Halfway along the narrow passageway Beatrice had made a decision. She would have to hide her true identity from Candy. After all, Candy was a very young kitten and not really all that bright. It would be too much to ask her to keep a secret, and Beatrice could not risk being unmasked in front of Grubsta. Besides, Beatrice was quite enjoying being Belladonna and was curious to find out more about her new dark side. And it would be fun to play a trick on Candy and see how long it took her to work out who her new roommate really was. In truth, Beatrice was also still quite cross with Candy for stealing Sheba's attention, not to mention usurping her own identity as Princess. And Belladonna turned out to be even more cross with her – though for different reasons.

"I 'ate snivellers," she announced scornfully, looking at the tiny woeful face before her. "So don't think you can get round me with a few tears."

Grubsta squeezed himself through the narrow gap and plopped into the room behind her. Candy wrinkled her nose in distaste at the smell and howled even louder.

"See 'ere," said Belladonna, undeterred, "The General's put me in charge of you, so you have to do as I say, right?"

Beatrice was gratified to see that her little friend's markings had stayed neatly in place in the time the two kittens had been apart but Candy did look very grubby and dishevelled and her plump tummy had become quite concave. None of this seemed to bother her alter ego, however.

"Now, my name's Belladonna which means poison and I poison little kittens that don't do as I say. So you'd better stop that snivelling sharp-ish or you won't get no supper neither."

Candy made an enormous effort and swallowed her sobs but Belladonna was just getting into her stride.

"An' another thing I 'ate is liars. An' you may be little, but from what I 'ear you're a great big liar. Pretending to be a princess!"

"I didn't…I never…" stammered poor Candy.

"No? Well, 'ow come you're 'ere then?"

"I don't kno-o-ow." Candy was about to start sobbing again but managed to catch her breath in time. "It was 'im, I mean *him*," she looked over at Grubsta. "He thought she was me – or I was her. And he just took me. Never even asked. I don't know how anyone could mistake me for Princess Beatrice." She looked down at her dirty fur in despair.

"I'm sure I don't know either," Belladonna said disdainfully. "It's alright Grubsta, you can get lost 'an all. We're OK 'ere."

Grubsta was so taken aback by her tone that he obeyed her without question. He really was stupid, Beatrice thought, watching his stinking rump disappearing into the dark.

"Any'ow," Belladonna turned back to Candy, "now there's just the two of us, tell me, what's so special about this Beatrice then? Them out there seem pretty desperate to get 'old of 'er."

Candy's eyes lit up and she stopped snivelling altogether.

"Oh, Beatrice is the most wonderful kitten you've ever met!"

"Really?" Belladonna's voice was scornful. "Why's that then? I don't 'old with royalty myself. I prefer a republic."

Candy looked blank. "Well, I don't know what a public is, but I know Beatrice and she's funny and incredibly clever.

191

She got my markings sorted out so that now I'm a proper p…p…pedigree. And she learnt me my grammar. Taught me, I mean." Candy corrected herself hastily. "And she knows the best games in town. I mean in the wood, of course."

"Well, I'm a proper street cat, so it's me as knows the best games in town and if you be'ave, I'll show you," said Belladonna. "Don't know no grammar though. Never needed it. But what does she look like then, this Beatrice? Is she beautiful, like a proper princess?"

Candy thought for a moment. "Well," she said at last, "not exactly."

Beatrice felt herself go cold with the dread of what she might be about to hear, but then Candy continued.

"She's…she's better than beautiful. I mean she's so interesting and exciting. You never know what she's going to look like from one minute to the next. Her markings move all the time, you see. They never stop."

"Really?" said Belladonna, with distaste. "How very peculiar. Sounds more like a circus animal than a Princess."

"Oh, but being beautiful all the time can be so boring!" In her enthusiasm Candy seemed to have quite forgotten her previous sadness. "Why the Princess, she can be anything she likes. She can be beautiful or funny or serious or plain. And sometimes," Candy's voice dropped to a whisper, "sometimes she can even be ugly, like…" she stopped herself and looked down at her filthy paws.

"Suppose you mean like me eh?" said Belladonna craftily. Beatrice did not know whether to be angry or delighted. The disguise was working even better than she could have imagined.

"Oh no, not like you." Candy corrected herself hastily. "Not like you at all. I just mean with the Princess, well you never knew what to expect. Watching those markings change was like hearing a story with good bits and bad bits and silly bits and sad bits. But the one thing that never really changed, you know? She was always kind – to me anyway." She sighed. "I miss her so much."

Beatrice wanted to leap on Candy and give her a big cuddle, not to mention a long, serious wash. But Belladonna was having none of it and so Beatrice's soft heart remained imprisoned along with her markings under Darius's magic spydernet. Even so, just listening to Candy's rapturous description of those markings made her think differently about them. There had been something quite exciting about those days when they had just done their own thing and chosen their own way. Now it was all down to her and she realised she did not have a clue what to do next. She hoped Belladonna had some ideas.

* * *

It was one thing being Belladonna around The General and Gangsta and Grubsta, but it was not so easy when it was only herself and Candy. There was something about Candy that made Beatrice feel kind and protective but each time she looked at her charge and her heart began to melt strange things happened. It began as a fluttery feeling, as though there was a tiny bird trapped inside her trying to escape. But then the bird could not get out because the markings would not move and so it turned into an angry buzzard which flapped its wings and tore at her from the inside, so that she was forced to race around the cave, jumping and howling, while little Candy cowered in a corner.

"Don't be such a scaredy-cat," Belladonna screeched at her. "Nothin' wrong with a bit of action now and again. You'll need to get used to worse than this if you're going to survive down 'ere. Else you'll end up going The Way of the Rabbit." She spat the last few words out.

"S…s…s…orry Belladonna." Candy's eyes were huge saucers in her pale face. "Which way did the rabbits actually go, then?"

"Down The General's throat!" Belladonna replied gleefully, "with the odd leg for Grub and Gangsta. Course 'e saves the 'eads special for me. Not that there's much brains to be 'ad from a rabbit of course. Bit like you really. But very tasty, all the same."

Candy froze with her belly to the floor. "Please don't let him eat me, Bella," she mewed piteously.

"Shouldn't think it'd be worth bothering with – scrawny little thing like you. Not even worth eating." Belladonna tossed her head in disgust. "Of course, there is something you could do which might make you safer."

"Anything, I'll do anything."

"You can tell 'im where to find the true Princess."

"Isn't she at home?" Candy looked puzzled.

"Apparently not. Those grubby foot soldiers went back, once they had realised their mistake. No one there. Only the mad old queen. What do they call her, Sheba? But she was completely out of her mind. Kept ranting about pyramids and passageways and screaming for cream all the time. Ran away when she saw them. Least, that's the way Gangsta told it. Wouldn't surprise me if it was the other way around and it was those two spivs that tailed it. From what I 'ear she's a bit of a dame."

Actually, Beatrice had heard nothing of the kind, but it seemed Belladonna was privy to a whole stash of information of which Beatrice was ignorant.

"Well, if Sheba doesn't know where Beatrice is, then no-body does," said Candy. "Sheba knows everything."

"Really?" Belladonna's voice was colder than the cave.

"Well, I guess so," Candy continued blithely ignoring the hostile response. "She doesn't just know about manners and Queen stuff. She knows about geography and history and places called Egypt and Babylon where they worshipped cats. And she knows what's going to happen in the future too."

"Sounds to me like she knows about telling lies. That must be where you get it from."

"No, no. It's not a lie!" Candy squeaked. "That's why I know Beatrice is extra special. Sheba told me one day Beatrice is going to be the greatest Queen the Wildwoods has ever seen. 'Course it's a secret so you mustn't tell no one. Specially not Beatrice."

"Why ever not? You'd think if she was so clever she'd 'ave worked it out for 'erself!" Beatrice had the distinct impression that Belladonna was enjoying this chance to have a secret dig at her.

"Sheba told me it was her job to bring Beatrice up properly. She said Beatrice had these powers, like, and if she wasn't careful she would grow up to be a..." Candy frowned in concentration.

"Yes?"

"I'm trying to remember. A d...d...a despot, that's it!"

"What's one of them when it's at 'ome then?"

Candy thought for a while. "I...I think it's a bit like The General, only worse."

"What, you mean like a cat with two iron legs instead of one?" Belladonna sneered.

"'Fraid I don't know." Candy shook her head sadly. "But that's why Sheba was so 'ard on 'er all the time. She said Beatrice 'ad to be a normal kitten, much as possible. Till she learned everything proper, like. Otherwise she would go mad with those markings. Or bad, which I think is worse."

"Mad or bad?" Belladonna licked her lips. "Sounds like my kind of cat. Better than a snooty Princess any day. Or a snivelling kitten. Which reminds me, it's time you were asleep."

"I'm too hungry to sleep," moaned Candy, who appeared to be growing less afraid of her new companion. "And I'm cold." She looked up hopefully. "I don't suppose there's any chance of a cuddle? To keep warm?"

"You suppose right. Bit of cold and hunger never did no harm. Hardens the bones, and the rest of you. Anyhow I might go out later. Now off you go into that corner." Belladonna indicated a particularly narrow, uncomfortable ledge. Candy looked crestfallen but did as she was told and curled up into a ball.

"Bella?"

"What now?"

"Sometimes you remind me of her."

"What, your poncy princess? I don't think so!"

"Just sometimes. It's like she's there just for a second, and then she's gone again."

"Hallucinations," said Belladonna severely. "Too many mice. I think you need a good fast day tomorrow. You been spoilt, I can tell. Bit of starvation's good for the soul. Now shut those dreadful blue eyes. And that mealy mouth. I've 'ad enough of you for today."

The quiet darkness was broken only by Candy's pathetic sniffs. Beatrice crouched on the damp stone and tried to reach within for the secret self that Candy had spied, for the soft hearted Princess she had once been. The one who had set off on this rescue mission to save her friends. But the blackness around and inside her was too dense. She could not feel herself. She could not feel a thing. It was like she had disappeared and only Belladonna was real, with her coldness and her cruelty. Candy might be the prisoner of The General but right now Beatrice felt like the prisoner of Belladonna.

And then she heard it, the scrabbling from behind the cave wall. It was a very faint sound at first – so faint that Beatrice had to listen not just with her ears but with her whole body. The net of spyder threads was definitely vibrating, and so was her fur underneath. The noise got louder. What could it mean?

Could it be Jake and Rufus on the other side? But they couldn't make a noise like that. It would have to be something bigger. Was there someone else? Someone trapped in another cave trying to get out? Or was there a monster – a proper monster, not like Cedric or Myrtle – trying to get in? What should she do? The trembling inside her must be Beatrice because Belladonna would not tremble, that was for sure. Still it was good to feel something again – even if it was only her own fear. She looked over at the sleeping Candy. There was no way she could take Candy with her and escape back the way she had come in. They would have to get through The General's cave and along all those passageways where she had been blindfolded. But she needed to find an escape route for them both.

Then she remembered the fork in the path leading from The General's cave to this one. Where did the other route lead? Maybe that was a way out. Could she risk leaving Candy? But sometimes it helped to be hard of heart. After all, Candy really was a very stupid kitten, and if it had not been for her preening herself like a Princess none of this would have happened in the first place. Candy would have to fend for herself for a few minutes and, come to that, so would the trembling Beatrice. This was a mission for Belladonna, the cunning street kitten. She felt herself darken even further, inside and out, even though her markings could no longer move. It was as though she had switched off all the lights in the world. No one would see her now.

CHAPTER 28
ROCKS AND A HARD PLACE

So it was Belladonna, the cunning street kitten, who climbed up the rock face, jumping from one ledge to another, swift and surefooted, while Beatrice just watched from somewhere inside. It was the weirdest feeling. Her stomach lurched as Bella leapt from rock to rock, her paws sliding on the slimy stones. But the nausea Beatrice felt was more than mere motion sickness.

Belladonna had started off as part of Beatrice. Beatrice had made Belladonna, created her out of her own mind and experience and imagination. Beatrice felt Bella's emotions as though they were her own. And yet, there was more to her, much more. Something separate and deeper, which Beatrice was only just beginning to understand.

Belladonna did not just look and sound like a stranger. She behaved and thought like one too. How else to explain that fearlessness and cunning, and the thrill that ran through her as she squeezed through the narrow opening at the top of the cave? Or the delight she took in her cruelty to Candy? What about those wild stories about the city? Were they actually true? And if so where did the knowledge come from?

The stone felt damp against her sides and the hard edges cut into her shoulders. Beatrice would have winced with the pain and yet Belladonna did not seem to notice it. Was that because she was simply a make-believe character who could not feel for herself, or because she actually was a street kitten, hardened to pain and hunger? In which case had Beatrice really made Belladonna up at all? Or had she always existed somewhere, with a life of her own? Would it even be possible to ask her? And, being Bella, would she tell the truth? In any case, this was not the time for conversation.

Belladonna had stopped and was sniffing the air. They had reached the top of Candy's cave and were now standing in a narrow passageway. Beatrice was aware of her whiskers tingling. It was not what she would call a breeze, just the slightest sensation of air moving, but it came as a relief. She had not realised how stale the air had been down in that cave. That meant they must be quite near the fork now. Belladonna stood like a statue, alert and listening. Hidden inside her, Beatrice listened too. Echoing along the stone corridor they heard the voice of The General.

"You! Greasy Grubsta! Get back out there in those woods and find us some proper grub. A few nice plump rabbits is what I need. And don't go telling me there's none left. Though now you've no tongue of course, so you can't be making excuses." They heard Gangsta's sycophantic laughter. But The General had not finished.

"If you don't find some food fast we're going to have to make do with those two scrawny kittens in there. There's no good information coming from them and there won't be much meat on them either, I'll warrant. But needs must. Now get going! Gangsta, you stay here, just in case I need reinforcements."

His iron leg clanked across the gritstone floor. Beatrice's fear dissolved before Belladonna's fury and indignation. The double crossing monster! They had offered to serve him and he just wanted them served up on a platter. Actually, there would not even be platter here of course, just a filthy floor strewn with rabbits' ears. They needed to work fast.

Beatrice would have been blinded by her emotions but Belladonna was focused, like a deadly missile. She headed onwards, stealthy and single-minded, which was remarkable given that, counting Beatrice, there were actually two minds at work at the same time. But Belladonna seemed able to ignore Beatrice when she chose, though it did not appear to work the other way around. Beatrice noticed this with trepidation but there did not seem to be much she could do about it right now. She needed Belladonna too much.

They headed onwards together and very soon came across the passageway they had been looking for. It sloped steeply away into the heart of the earth. Rocks jutted out from the sides and the ceiling and they had to duck and weave to avoid them. Round a corner, over a stream and down a steep drop with rough, stone steps they came to the end.

It was a tiny space, only about two cats high and four cats wide. The air smelt rank, like a death chamber. Beatrice had never been in a death chamber but Belladonna recognised it immediately. Another part of her secret life, thought Beatrice. But she had no time to reflect on what this might mean because her attention was taken by something much more important and unexpected. There, crouched in the corner, half dead and half alive was a familiar figure. Beatrice felt her heart turn over and then drop, like a stone falling deep into the quarry.

"Rufus? Is that you?" The voice that came out sounded like Belladonna's, deep and croaky, but it belonged to Beatrice. It carried love and shock and fear and sadness.

"Rufus?" she said again.

The cat in the corner flinched. His beautiful green eyes glittered unnaturally with fear and hunger. But he did not reply.

"Roof, it's me!"

The cat looked up, but his gaze seemed to go right through her, as though she was not there. When he spoke his voice was so weak Beatrice could hardly hear him.

"I'm terribly sorry. I can't see you all that well in this god-forsaken darkness, but I don't think we have been introduced."

Beatrice's frustration only made her markings darker, if that were possible.

"Of course you do!" She could feel her own voice now, breaking through Belladonna's and she tried to make it bright and jolly. "It's me, here inside. This is just the safety net Darius made for me."

"I'm afraid I don't know any Darius." Rufus's manners were as impeccable as ever but he clearly found it an effort to speak.

"Of course you don't. I forgot, you fell off the train before we met him – when I was only just beginning to manage my markings. Oh Roof, you should just see what I can do with them now." But even as she spoke she wondered exactly who was in charge of her markings at the moment. Beatrice or Belladonna?

"I'm not sure I…" Rufus eyed her more closely. "Can it be you? Really? Beatrice? Oh I am ever so sorry, I meant Your Royal Highness." Rufus had struggled onto all fours and was doing his best to bow.

"Oh don't be so stupid, Roof!" Belladonna's sharp tones made Rufus start. Poor thing, thought Beatrice, he's obviously been through it.

"I'm sorry, Roof, I'm obviously not managing them all that well, as you can see. Sometimes they still have a mind of their own."

"And they seem to have acquired a mouth of their own too." Rufus managed a faint smile.

"Oh don't mind her. She's Belladonna. Just a part of my disguise. Ouch!" The spydernet had suddenly contracted so tight around Beatrice's throat that she could not speak.

"I'm sure she's very clever, very…inventive," Rufus almost managed a smile. The spydernet relaxed. Beatrice could breathe again. She must remember to be careful what she said about Belladonna in future.

"But how on earth did you end up here?" The two old

friends spoke at exactly the same time. There was a pause, then they both laughed.

"You first."

"No, you, Your Highness."

So Beatrice told him about Maverico and the spyders and how Jake had gone off with Sergeant Pepper in search of Rufus and how she had disguised herself as a Bad Cat to win The General's trust. As she told her story and Rufus listened she noticed that her own natural voice was returning, little by little.

"I'm not sure my plan has worked out worked so well," she added sheepishly. "It is all much harder than I thought. But at least I've found Candy. And now you, Rufus."

"Ah, Candy's here then," said Rufus. "I feared as much. I only see Grubsta once a day and he doesn't say a lot."

"He can't, he's got no tongue," said Beatrice. "The General cut it out as punishment for kidnapping Candy instead of me."

Rufus recoiled in horror. "That Grubsta's a rough old chap, but really!"

"Now, Roof, what about you? How did you end up here?"

Rufus sighed. "Well, you know, just as we started going downhill on that train I thought I saw Leon again and I got rather excited and lost my balance. I do have trouble from time to time with my vertigo. Anyway, after I landed I looked again, and I kept thinking I'd seen him so I followed in the direction I thought he'd gone. But then he just disappeared. Next thing I knew it was like the ground gave way beneath my feet and I fell through the earth and landed right in front of The General. In that extraordinary cave."

"It is pretty weird," said Beatrice, shivering at the memory. "But I don't remember seeing any holes in the ceiling."

"No, the entrance is kept covered by a couple of dead crows with their wings spread out. More of a trap than an entrance, I suppose."

"Oh, that's why they're there." Beatrice thought back to the feathers and beaks and tails which littered The General's cave and the dead birds, hanging from the ceiling like a macabre chandelier.

"Of course I fought, but Gangsta and Grubsta were there too, so it was three to one. Then The General finished the job off and knocked me out completely with his iron leg. When I woke up I was here. They must have carried me some of the way. Then I think they just threw me down those stone steps and left me. That would account for the bruises."

"Oh, poor Rufus. Doesn't Grub bring you any food?"

"No, he just stands at the top and stares at me. Spits sometimes. I can get a bit of water by licking the wet walls. But, oh Bee, it's so good to see you. Even looking like that."

Beatrice noted that, for the first time ever, Rufus had used Jake's familiar term of address. Bee. But he was clearly not himself, so she decided to let it pass.

"Roof, we need a plan. There are three of us now, with Candy, though two of us are kittens and you don't look fit for much. Well, maybe there are four of us, if you count Belladonna."

"Exactly who is this Belladonna, Your Highness? She sounds quite intriguing."

"Do you know Roof, I only wish I knew." Beatrice sighed. "I thought she was just me in disguise. But now I'm not so sure. It's like I've got this other person inside me that's hard and cruel and yet brave and strong. Or maybe I'm inside her. I can't tell any more. Maybe we can talk about it next time. I have to go and check on Candy now. But I'll be back real soon. Think, hard!"

"Of course, Your Highness."

"But Roof?"

"Yes, Your Highness?"

"One thing I don't understand. If Jake and Sergeant Pepper

203

followed you down that hole, how come they are not here too?" But Rufus did not reply. His legs had buckled beneath him and his eyes were closed. Clearly, they did not have much time left.

* * *

Beatrice arrived back to find Candy cowering on her ledge, her spine pressed to the wall. She was shaking with terror.

"Oh Bella, thank heavens you're here, but where've you been? There's something behind the wall and it's trying to get in. Oh Help! Help! It's going to eat us up."

"For heaven's sake, keep that noise down!" Belladonna cuffed Candy hard on both sides of the head. "If the monster didn't know you were here before, he certainly does now. Now lie down and shut that mouth."

The darkness of the cave was broken only by the flash of Candy's white belly as it heaved with silent sobs. Belladonna disappeared into the shadows. And Beatrice disappeared once more into Belladonna.

CHAPTER 29

FRIENDS REUNITED

"Oh good, I'm starving!"

Candy was eyeing the two dead voles and the single rabbit head which Grubsta had deposited at the mouth of their cave. It was probably early morning, Beatrice thought, though it was difficult to tell day from night in this place. Echoing through the tunnels came the screams of another rabbit, about to be decapitated.

Beatrice's stomach contracted with hunger and her mouth watered at the thought of breakfast. At the same time she kept seeing the baby rabbit she had rescued, with its silly, twitchy nose and its soft, shivering fur. There was something about the image of the rabbit that reminded her of Candy. Would she ever be able to eat rabbit again? Perhaps she should become a vegan like Dino.

Belladonna, however, had no time for such scruples, and was more interested in torturing little Candy.

"Remember what I said," she announced gleefully. "Today's a fast day for you. Now don't start snivelling again or I'll give you something to snivel about. You should 'ave behaved yourself when I told you. Now you'll go 'ungry. Won't do a little cissy like you no 'arm to learn what life's really like." She sniffed the food ostentatiously. "Mmmm these look delicious. An' you stay here and behave, or there'll be no tea tomorrow neither!"

"Why, where are you going? Please Bella! Don't take them away. I'm starving!"

Belladonna crammed both the voles and the rabbit head into her mouth all at once so that the rabbit's ears and the voles' tails hung down at either side of her chin, making her look rather like a walrus. She growled loudly through her full mouth and Candy jumped back in alarm.

Beatrice could feel the pleasure Belladonna took in Candy's terror and she felt ashamed. Could this person truly be a part of her? And yet at the same time Belladonna was helping Beatrice to help Rufus and Candy, so she couldn't be all bad, could she?

As if to prove a point Belladonna picked out one of the voles from between her teeth and tossed it carelessly in Candy's direction before heading out of the cave. Beatrice could feel her ugly companion twitching with irritation at the kindness she had been forced to show and felt gratified. Perhaps things would become easier between them. Perhaps Beatrice was in charge after all.

"Where are you going, Bella?" Candy squealed. "Are you going somewhere to eat those all by yourself?"

Belladonna never replied. She was furious with Beatrice and hollow with hunger. Her mouth watered at the delicious taste of rabbit in her mouth, but she fought the urge to bite down. Beatrice might moan and feel faint with not eating – might even sneak the last vole if no one was looking. But Belladonna was a streetcat and a warrior, used to going days without food if need be. And today was such a day. There was a task to be done. Hunger could wait. She headed silently off up the stone passageway, intent on her mission, ignoring the complaints from Beatrice's belly and the sobs from Candy which followed her through the darkness.

* * *

When they found Rufus again he was lying on the floor licking the water off the sides of the cave, too weak even to stand.

206

"Here you are Roof. It's not much but it's all we could manage."

It was Beatrice, not Belladonna, who laid the vole and the rabbit head on the floor in front of him. Though Belladonna might have the upper hand when Candy and Grubsta were around, it seemed that just the sight of Rufus was enough to restore Beatrice to herself. She spoke with her normal voice again and in her own accent. But then Rufus himself was so gentle and courteous that she could not imagine anyone being uncouth for long when they were near him.

"Eat these. You'll feel better soon."

Rufus looked at her and was about to say something but she stopped him.

"Don't speak, Roof. At least not till you've eaten."

And so he ate, slowly and carefully, while Beatrice sat and watched, trying not to think about the strange sensations in her own belly. She was aware of Belladonna taking a grim pleasure in her discomfort. More worryingly, she felt Belladonna's coldness towards poor Rufus. Thoughts and phrases kept springing unbidden into her consciousness – words like *nancy-boy* and *coward* and *weak* and *feeble,* all spoken in Belladonna's harsh tones. She pushed them down determinedly, forcing herself to remember Rufus's former strength and elegance, his thoughtfulness and integrity. But a feeling of nausea overwhelmed her and she knew it came from Belladonna.

Eventually, when everything was gone, apart from the inedible parts of the vole's intestines, Rufus licked his lips and gave a great sigh.

"Your Royal Highness, I can never thank you enough."

"Don't thank me. Just listen to me for a bit."

Beatrice had spent a lot of time thinking during her time in the dungeon.

"We need to get you strong enough to help us fight our way out of here. And I need to find a way of getting us all some food. Maybe I can persuade The General to let me out with Gangsta one day."

Rufus smiled, weakly.

"Perhaps, Your Highness. I will certainly do my best to serve you. But do you think you can get out without raising suspicion?"

"I might not, but Belladonna can," said Beatrice.

About time said a familiar voice in her head. *Wait around all day for you two to do anything.* The nausea left her as she felt Belladonna, happy now, alert and alive and excited at the prospect of adventure.

"I just wish I knew where Jake and Rico are," she sighed.

"Rufus!" A tiny voice behind her squealed with delight. "Is it you? And Bella? So this is where you went."

Beatrice turned round and looked up. Candy was standing at the top of the steep steps.

"How dare you follow me without permission!" Belladonna's deep voice burst out, taking both Beatrice and Rufus by surprise. Her tail swished wildly, spreading its darkness throughout the tiny room and hitting Rufus on the head.

"Ah, Candy," said Rufus, rising to the occasion despite his weakness, "I am afraid I am a little indisposed. Our friend here – Belladonna, I believe she is called – was just bringing me something to eat."

"Oh, so that's where our tea went." Candy sounded relieved. "I thought she'd eaten it herself. Sorry, Bella. See, now I know you're not as mean as you make out. But Rufus, where you've been? You'll have to tell me all about it."

"No 'e won't. Not now. 'E's far too weak. And just so's you know, this little gift of ours, it's just between ourselves – understand? No blabbin' to Grubsta or Gangsta. An' no leavin' that cave again unless I say so, geddit?" Belladonna gave Candy her meanest look.

"No Bella. It's just, well, that noise, that scrabbling, it's getting louder. I can't 'elp it. I get real scared. Specially when you're not there."

"Well you may have to get used to it. If we are going to build your friend 'ere back up to strength and not starve ourselves then I'll 'ave to find a way of getting out. Can't rely on the rations they're giving us, that's for sure."

"And when I'm stronger, then I can be of some assistance," Rufus interjected.

"Hmmm, let's hope so." Belladonna looked him up and down critically, like a farmer appraising cattle while Beatrice cringed with embarrassment. "So if you've quite finished stuffing your face and gossiping I need to be getting back to sort this mess out."

* * *

Candy was right, the noise was getting louder but Belladonna was having none of it.

"Lot of stuff and nonsense! Us streetcats ain't scared of nothin'," she declared roundly.

Beatrice felt fear bubbling up inside her. If it was not a monster, could it be something worse? A prisoner walled up, trying desperately to get out? Maybe Jake or Maverico were trapped? She went cold at the thought but Belladonna carried on scolding Candy regardless.

"Now soon as Grubsta's done the mouse drop I want you back on that ledge young lady. An' if you don't go straight to sleep I'll knock one of them loose rocks on your head." She indicated a few precariously balanced stones jutting out from the ceiling. "Then you'll be out good an' proper."

* * *

It was an hour or so later when Grubsta arrived, bringing with him two scrawny mice. Just as he began to lay them down on the floor the scrabbling started again. Belladonna saw his ears prick up and sprang into action, clawing loudly at the rock face to disguise the sound.

"Got to keep my claws in good shape, you know, so's I can give this one a sharp scratch if I need to."

She eyed Candy then looked across at Grubsta and winked. Grubsta winked back salaciously, then backed up against a rock and sprayed, long and loud. Candy caught her breath. Beatrice felt like vomiting but Belladonna just laughed.

"Now be off with you, you rascal," she replied, archly, "and leave us two ladies to rest."

Three ladies really, thought Beatrice – though Belladonna could hardly be called a lady. But Grubsta did as he was told and left obediently, with a quick backward glance when he reached the top and a last, grubby wink.

"Blimey, I thought' 'e'd never go," said Belladonna.

Beatrice was not sure if Belladonna was talking to herself or to Beatrice or, for that matter whether there was any difference between the two.

"Bella," Candy's voice came from high up on the ledge where she had settled according to instructions, "why did you pretend there wasn't a monster behind those walls? If you hadn't scratched like that he might have realised and let us out."

"Because I told you there isn't one," screeched Belladonna furiously.

Beatrice saw Candy flinch in terror and decided it was time to intervene. "If you like I'll sing you a lullaby," she said in a voice that was not quite hers and not quite Belladonna's either. She could tell that Belladonna was seething at the interruption because her belly heaved with nausea.

"Oh Bella, that would be lovely." Candy's eyes were huge and dark in her tiny face.

It was only then Beatrice realised she didn't know any lullabies. And heaven only knew what Belladonna's musical repertoire might be. But there was one song she could re-member. It was not really suitable but it would just have to do. Beatrice took a deep breath and began to sing.

> *That I, who am descended from Queens of Egypt,*
> *Whose ancestors enjoyed sand and sunshine,*
> *Temples and pyramids,*
> *Who ate with Pharaohs*
> *Who slept on silk sheets…*

"Bella," Candy's voice was faint and sleepier, "that's Sheba's song. She sang it to me in the woods. How come…"

"What did I say?" hissed Belladonna. "One more word and those rocks above you, they'll be down on your head!"

There was silence as Beatrice took up the refrain once more. Who would have imagined that the Sheba's lament might actually be reassuring? Beatrice sang Candy to sleep and then she sang herself to sleep, dreaming of sand and sunshine and a comforting, untidy attic. Only Belladonna stayed awake and watchful.

* * *

Beatrice awoke from her sweet dreams to a loud crash. The wall from which the scrabbling had come was beginning to collapse. From the ledge above came a terrified squeal. The shock had dislodged all the precariously balanced stones with which Belladonna had been threatening Candy and one of them had indeed hit her on the head. After the squeal there was silence. From below, Beatrice could not see where Candy was, but in any case she was too distracted by what was happening in front of her to worry about her little charge.

Out of the gaping hole in the wall stepped one of the largest creatures Beatrice had ever seen. It looked a bit like a dog only much broader, with heavy, thickset limbs, a powerful body and a black and white striped face that reminded Beatrice of her own markings. And sitting astride this terrifying beast, crouched on top, with his front paws almost round its neck and his bottom in the air, was Jake. Lovely, big, cuddly Jake. Once more she felt her markings straining against the spydernet, her love so overwhelming it threatened to burst out.

"Why, howdy, Miss Bee. It sure does my heart good to see you."

Beatrice's eyes filled with tears. They were the only part of her not restrained by Darius's netting which, must have been why Jack Daw had said they were a dead giveaway. It felt so good just to be Bee again. Not Belladonna. Not even Beatrice. Just Bee – with Jake. And to be recognised for who she was, despite all the ugly markings and the ugly thoughts and the dark hole she still felt at her centre. Even Rufus had not recognised her in her spydernet. But Jake knew her deep down, in places where she did not even always know herself.

"Jake! So you're the monster!"

"Well, that's no way to greet an old friend," he laughed, "let alone one that's dug through miles of tunnels to get here."

"Excuse me!" The great hairy black and white beast beneath him shook himself with such force that Jake fell off. The creature puffed himself up indignantly till he nearly filled the entire cave. "As I recall, it was me and my army that did the actual digging. You just sat around making sarcastic comments."

"Helpful suggestions, I'd call them," said Jake. "But my dear sweet Bee, you've never met a real live badger before have you? This here fine gentleman is King Billy, overseer of Badger City, which I think I told you about. I hope you are both royally pleased to meet each other."

"Delighted, I'm sure," replied Beatrice, deeply embarrassed by her ugly appearance. "Though from what my mother told me I understand I do have sovereignty over your kingdom." She paused for a minute. "Or at least I will when I am myself again."

She could feel Belladonna's fury at the betrayal, her common, gravelly voice fighting to make its way out, ready to chide and lie and boast and to accuse her publicly of treachery. Was it not, after all, Belladonna and not Beatrice who had done all the hard work, taken the risks, tricked The General and his cohort, discovered Candy and even found Rufus and fed him? Well, she would have to deal with that later. Beatrice swallowed hard and tried to feel her own softness, the softness she always felt around Jake and Rufus and Maverico. Being Belladonna was hard in every sense of the word. But being Beatrice with Belladonna around was pretty tough too.

"Oh, my Princess, I am honoured to serve you of course." King Billy stretched his front paws out and bowed his head low to the ground. "These past few months since Leon's passing have been a terrible time for the Wildwoods. A time of tyranny, cruelty and recklessness indeed."

"Months?" asked Beatrice. "But we saw him pass only a few days ago. Well, maybe not exactly pass. He was a bit ahead of us." Beatrice's voice trailed away. How long had she been here? How long had she been away from home? "But anyway," she turned to Jake, "how did you know where to find me?"

"Well, it was Darius. He got a message through the web to Sergeant Pepper about what you had planned."

"But the last I saw you, you were going down the hole after Rufus. Oh Jake, poor Rufus, he's here and he can hardly move and I think they are trying to starve him to death."

Jake's white whiskers set in a grim line. "Ain't no one goin' to starve on my watch." He paused for a moment before beginning his story.

"See, those spyders, they lowered me down that hole, an' we kept goin' lower an' lower an' then we heard The General shouting and stamping that iron foot and ragin' about Candy bein' a fake and Rufus bein' for the dungeon. An' we didn't right well know where you was but we figured the best thing was to go back up again and work out what to do next. A bit of a load on them poor spyders, haulin' me back up, mind you.

"But at least we knowed where The General's cave was, an' Sergeant Pepper, he sent a couple of the littlest spyders down as intelligence – spydinis they call 'em. So they worked out where everything was an' where you were an' then it was down to my good friend here an' his noble warriors."

"It was nothing, Your Highness," King Billy bowed again. "And once we have driven the Bad Cats out this will do very nicely as a new suburb of Badger City – with your permission of course. We are getting a little crowded in our current accommodation."

"How are we going to drive them out then?" Beatrice looked from the big badger to Jake. "Roof can hardly stand, let alone fight. The General never comes down here cos he can't walk and you'll never get through that narrow passageway. You are way too big, King Billy. And you Jake are way too fat. But what about Rico?"

"Rico's preparing reinforcements. We'll talk about that in a minute. So where's Candy?"

Beatrice looked up at the ledge guiltily. She had been so excited to see Jake she had quite forgotten the kitten who had caused all this furore in the first place.

"She's up there. I think she may have been knocked out when those rocks fell. But she doesn't know who I am. She thinks I'm a street cat called Belladonna."

"I *am* a streetcat called Belladonna," yelled a deep, scary voice from somewhere inside Beatrice. "And I am a least as real as you."

"Indeed you are Sweet Bee, if that's who you wanna Bee." Jake seemed unperturbed by the interruption as though two voices spoke out of one body all the time. "Though I can think of more exciting and exotic options myself," he drawled.

"Believe me, Big Boy, I can be exciting and exotic when I want." Belladonna rubbed herself against Jake's broad flanks suggestively. He smiled in appreciation and she bit him hard on the tail.

"Ow! Easy tiger!" Jake winced, then grinned. Beatrice was amazed to see that he seemed to find her situation amusing.

"When you've all finished," said King Billy rather testily, "I think you might like to take a look at this."

Blood was dripping onto the rocks just beneath the ledge where Candy had been sleeping. Jake climbed up to take a look while Beatrice fought an internal battle with Belladonna who was desperate to go and lick up the blood herself.

"She's injured and unconscious but she's still breathing." Jake's voice came from the ledge. A few minutes later he emerged carrying Candy by the scruff of her neck and passed her to King Billy, who took her tenderly in his powerful jaws.

"Can you carry her to Sheba's cave for me, Billy?" asked Jake. "She'll know what to do."

"Sheba's what?" squeaked Beatrice. "You mean she's down here too. Has The General got her?"

Jake shook his head as the big badger departed. "No, no, I'd like to see him try. We'll talk about that later. Now you and me, we need to make a plan."

* * *

The next time Grubsta came to do his late night checks, Belladonna was waiting for him. She positioned herself right at the entrance to the cave and fluffed herself up so that he could not see where Candy was or, indeed, the gaping hole in the back wall.

"Ssshh!" she said to him, although, since Grubsta could

215

not speak this was a bit of an irrelevance. "Don't come in or you'll wake 'er." She nodded her head conspiratorially over to a particularly dingy corner.

"I 'ad the devil of a job gettin' 'er to sleep. She's got it in 'er 'ead there are monsters in 'ere. As if!" Belladonna rolled her eyes in exasperation. "Any'ow, I need to come back with you tonight. Got to 'ave a word with The General about something."

Grubsta stood looking at her and not moving, as though he was trying to decide whether he was being duped or not.

"Well, go on then. Move along."

Belladonna's voice had just a touch of threat in it. She shoved him hard with her head and eventually he turned and began making his way through the passageway back to The General. Belladonna followed. He kept looking over his shoulder suspiciously. She tried winking again but this time it did not have the same effect as earlier. He just kicked her head with his back legs, the tunnel being too narrow to allow him to turn around and do the job properly. She contented herself with spitting back. She would show him. All in good time.

The General's cave was full of corpses and furs and feathers as before. The dead crows were still hanging from the ceiling and she could just make out the hole through which Rufus had fallen. Quite a fetching arrangement, and very clever, though a waste of a few good meals. Prissy Beatrice, of course, was horrified at that thought. Well, she would just have to toughen up if they were going to see this thing through.

"What's she doin' here? Did I give you permission to leave?"

The General stomped his leg hard on the ground so the piles of beaks rattled and the eyeballs quivered like jelly. Belladonna stepped forward with a swagger.

"Pardon me, Your Excellency, but I 'ave a suggestion and poor old Grub 'ere couldn't exactly tell it to you now could 'e?"

"And what suggestion could you possibly have – unless you are thinking of passing on a few nice recipes for kitten stew?"

Belladonna looked at him. He was definitely skinnier than he had been a few days ago and a hungry cat was a dangerous creature.

"Thing is, Your Excellency, I did 'ear as you were a bit short on the old rabbit front. We certainly 'aven't 'ad any – well, just that 'ead, like – and you don't look too fat yourself, if you don't mind my saying. Well, turns out I might know where there's a secret stash of rabbits. What do you call it? A warren, that's it."

"You do?" The General stomped towards her and stood over her so his iron leg was right in front of her nose. "Well, why don't you tell us about it then, and save your skin? Not much flesh on you left to save, is there?" He bared his teeth in what might almost have been a smile.

"Well, see, I'm new to the woods, so I don't rightly know 'ow to direct you. But I think I could find it again, like, if I was out there."

There was a silence while The General considered the logic of this.

"If you don't trust me," Belladonna continued, "you could always send Gangsta with me. That way we could bring more of 'em back. Two mouths are better than one, as they say."

The General chewed his tail for a few minutes. His shoulders twitched with fleabites. She could see how thin he was around the haunches.

"OK, then. Just this once. But you'd better behave. Soon as Gangsta's back you can take him with you. And just remember," he leered at her hungrily, "if you don't bring any rabbits back, then it's you and that fluffy-head in there for the pot, instead."

217

CHAPTER 30
THE GAME OF THE NAME

"You get behind me till we get out of the labyrinth. Don't want you go 'atching no escape plot." Gangsta's one eye was full of contempt and loathing. He curled his lips in distaste displaying a single yellow fang which was chipped at the end.

"Whatever you say, boss. The view's better from this direction anyway."

Beatrice was shocked by Belladonna's insolence but she could not help being impressed too. While Beatrice shrank fearfully into her spydernet, Belladonna thrilled with excitement. Danger was her element.

"That's enough, sewer-cat." Gangsta spat so hard his spittle landed on Belladonna's face. "Now shut those jaws or I'll shut 'em for you."

"Well, that's very nice, innit?" Belladonna was enjoying herself. "Right, I won't say another word. Not one. I'll be nice and quiet like one of them poncy good cats. Or that Princess you're after. Bet she's not got a lot to say for 'erself. Leastways, nothing worth listening to. Can't think why you want to be bothered with 'er myself. No experience of life. No spine probably neither.

"Still I know what you mean. Nothin' more annoying than folk talking all the time. Some people, though, they just can't shut up, can they? Whatever you say to them, they just keep on talking."

Gangsta swung round, growling. His jaws dripped with foul-smelling saliva.

"Ok, Ok, silence it is." Belladonna licked the spittle off her cheek like it was cream. "Just 'aving a bit of fun."

Beatrice would have been furious if she had not known that it would make Belladonna happy to see her angry. Besides she had other things on her mind. Things Jake had told her the previous evening which meant the battle ahead would be much more dangerous and complicated than she could have imagined.

Out of the corner of her eye she saw a tiny spyder scurrying along next to them. This must be one of the spydinis Jake had talked about. Attached to his microscopic midriff was a fine silk thread which waved and vibrated as they moved. These threads were part of what Darius called the wood-wide web – an intelligence network which ran throughout the wood above ground. Jake simply called it the bush telegraph. "A bit like smoke signals back home, Bee, 'cept it uses vibrations." This was the first time the spyders were risking using it underground in The General's territory.

"If The General discovers what they are doing we are all done for," Jake had told her.

"I don't get it, Jake." Beatrice had had a lot of time to think in the dungeon. "If there are only three bad cats and everyone hates them, then how can they rule the Wildwoods?"

"Well, Bee, that's true, of course." Jake looked a little embarrassed. "Guess there's a few things I ain't told you yet 'bout this here situation we've got ourselves into. Tell the truth, I didn't right understand it myself at first. Not sure I do now actually.

"See, The General, he ain't got no friends here, that's right. But he has plenty elsewhere. Not that I'd exactly call them friends.

"Seems like when he got caught in the Time Tunnel he made a bargain with the Powers Beneath. They're the ones that rule down there. He said he'd give them his leg if they would give him back his freedom."

"That sounds a fair exchange," said Beatrice.

"Well, maybe. 'Cept it wasn't no freedom. The General is at their mercy now. And believe me, Bee, you don't want to cross the Powers Beneath. Or their friends. It's them I'm mostly worried about to tell the truth."

"Why? Who are these friends? What's so bad about them?" Beatrice had never seen Jake look so worried.

"No friends of ours, Bee," he said, gravely. "And they ain't got no names neither. That's why they are known simply as the Nameless."

"I don't understand," said Beatrice. "Everything has a name. My mother always said that a name was a sacred thing because it contained the essence of your soul. I mean, even the creatures we met when we went through the Time Tunnel all had names – Dino and Cedric and Myrtle.

"And I've got several. There's Beatrice and Beattie." She shuddered a little at the memory of The Lady's ridiculous pet name for her. Now it just felt like a sign of captivity. "And you call me Bee. And now there's Belladonna too. Though I'm not altogether sure that she is really me, so she might not count."

Jake laughed. "Oh, she counts alright. That's just it Bee. You are special in lots of ways. And you have lots of names. So with Belladonna you have a name for what we might call your darker side. And maybe you'll have some more names somewhere for a few more sides you don't know about yet. But you're clever and you're getting wiser and you can use them all.

"Sheba was right, though. Names are important. I guess havin' a name for something helps you to talk to it, maybe even listen to it. Pay it some respect, any road. But the Nameless Ones are made up of all the bad thoughts and feelings nobody wants to recognise or accept. No one wants to talk or listen to them. Or even admit they exist. They're just all stored up. Well, not even stored up, I guess. They are just somewhere out there waiting to make themselves known."

"So are they trying to steal our names?" Beatrice was remembering her mother's dark warnings.

"Not exactly. From what I understand, it's more like they're looking for a name to latch onto. Which means anyone with a name is a target. Then they sort of take you over.

"They'll catch you unawares. You'll be thinking nice, kind thoughts or maybe enjoying a simple scratch and the next thing you're full of hatred and anger, and you'll take it out on 'most anyone or anythin' as happens to be passin'. You might shout or scream. You might do something real spiteful, like steal someone's mouse supper. Or you might even kill them.

"We've all got some of the Nameless hidin' in our heads and generally we can manage 'em, or we give 'em a name – like anger or sadness or fear or malice, or even a proper one like Belladonna. Least then you can start a dialogue, like, you know, come to an agreement. Well you know that better than any of us, BellaBee. Though I reckon you two haven't come to full agreement yet." He grinned. "Need to give it a bit of time. But down the in Time Tunnel there's millions of 'em. Enough to start a world war. And now they've escaped.

"Mostly it's the folk who think they're good as gets taken over cos they don't know to watch out. The General, like, he was a good guy at first. Strong and brave. But he was ambitious too. He was jealous of Leon, but he couldn't admit that, even to himself. Told himself a different story – like that Leon was weak and that the Wildwoods would be better if he was in charge. That was how he ended up going down the Time Tunnel in the first place, so's he could rule the woods for all time.

"Then once he'd done his deal to get free and the Tunnel was open it was easy for the hundreds and thousands of Nameless just to tag onto him. When the Tunnel is closed tight they can't get out. But once it's opened then the Nameless can escape.

"They are out there now looking for someone, anyone, to fix onto. Cats, foxes, rats, squirrels – they're not fussy. That's why King Billy is so eager to help. They've had one or two badgers gone bad recently – done a lot of harm."

Beatrice was struggling to understand. "But why didn't it happen to us? How do we know we didn't bring them back as well as The General? After all, we went through the Time Tunnel too."

"That's true and it was a big risk – no doubt about it," Jake agreed. "But what Leon always told me was that a pure heart stood the best chance of passing through safely. He said there's always a risk with time travel, cos you're goin' against the natural order, like. But he reckoned if you travel in love then you won't get harmed and you won't harm anythin'. We were not looking for anythin' for ourselves, see. We were looking for Candy. And I guess that's the difference.

"'Course now we're through and they're through and we're all here, that protection's gone. It's every cat for himself – or herself, I should say."

"So, if we just gave these Nameless things a name – like Belladonna or even Cedric – would that make it alright?"

Jake shook his head. "I wish it were that simple, Bee. For it to work properly we would have to reunite all the Nameless with their rightful named person – that's to say the one who had those feelings in the first place. And then we'd have to get them to give those feelings their real name and face up to them. To take them back – a bit like you and Belladonna. Not many people are up for that. It's quite a challenge as you know.

"For now we need to drive them back down the Tunnel and make sure it's closed and to do that we have to send The General back, I'm afraid. Till we do, the Nameless will tag on to anything that has a name. So remember that when you are out there with Rico. Be on guard, even if somebody seems good and kind. Especially, perhaps, if they seem good and kind."

"Ok, we're out now. But you'd better stick close Hells-Bells or it won't be rabbit we're eating tonight."

Beatrice snapped out of her reverie abruptly. She would need all her wits about her – and all of Belladonna's wits too – for the task that lay ahead.

It was a clear night. The woods looked quite different from the last time Beatrice had been outside. All the leaves had dropped to the ground and the tree trunks stood like skeletons, their bones and joints exposed to the cold. They reminded Beatrice of the poor broken bones that lined the Time Tunnel.

The sky was vast and sparkling. The air was heady with scents – leaves and fungus and mice and rats and birds and sheep and stone and damp wood. She thought she could even smell the stars. It was a scent that danced on her nose and tickled her whiskers and felt very hot and very cold at the same time. There was so much to see and smell and feel that Beatrice found the experience overwhelming but, fortunately for her, Belladonna remained focused, her ears lifted, her eyes searching the trees around.

"So where are the bats, big boy?" she asked Gangsta. "Didn't see many of them in the city. I'd like to take a good look."

"Hibernating, of course," Gangsta said, scornfully. "Don't you know nothin', street cat? Far too cold for them in winter. They'll be 'angin' upside down in some rock somewhere, dreamin' of summertime. Now the bunnies, they 'ave to come out to eat, just like us. So come on, where are they? Let's see if you were telling the truth."

Beatrice felt a shiver of dread run through her. Jake had said Maverico was depending on the bats for help. He had not mentioned hibernation. Maybe bats didn't hibernate where Maverico came from and so he didn't know about it.

"Jus' give me a minute, laddo. I'm tryin' to get my bearings." Belladonna said, bossily. To Beatrice's surprise, the tactic worked. Gangsta was obviously used to taking orders. He stood quietly while Belladonna looked and sniffed and listened.

Inside the spydernet Beatrice was also searching – not just for rabbits and Maverico but also for the Nameless Ones. The only trouble was she had no idea what to look for. Jake seemed to think they were invisible, so they probably did not smell of anything either.

Something whooshed past her ear, screeching loudly. Her heart trembled with an emotion which was more than simple fear. The creature had not touched her and yet she felt she had been struck by a force that that was cold and angry and full of hate. This must be how the Nameless felt, surely. Further away there was a loud scream. Then another and another. The sounds threatened to tear the woods apart.

"Those foxes are noisy." Gangsta looked edgy as he gazed ahead. "Don't know what's bothering them but I gotta say something feels weird here tonight."

For Gangsta to notice, Beatrice thought, it must be very weird indeed. But he was right. There was a tension, a tautness in the air – as though the whole wood was holding its breath. As though a thousand secret eyes were watching them.

She heard a rustling in the scrubby grass. The curves of a snake shimmered in the moonlight. Its scales were black diamonds, its red eyes glittered like rubies. Looking into them Beatrice felt she was entering the swamp all over again, only this time Jake was not here to turn it into a game and make it safe. She was going to get sucked down and eaten up. Unless?

"Good evening, Cedric," she whispered timidly, hoping Gangsta could not hear.

To her surprise the snake reared up and then bowed its head low to the ground, so that it made a half-hoop, just like the giant sea-serpent had done. She caught a glimpse of forked tongue, then one red eye closed slowly. Was this a mini-Cedric? And was it really winking at her?

"Nice one, Bee," she heard Belladonna whisper, and felt ridiculously pleased.

The next moment a rabbit broke cover from behind a tree, then another. Suddenly, there were rabbits everywhere, all running in different directions, their white tails bobbing.

"Looks like he's the boss. Watch me take him out," said Gangsta, heading off after the largest rabbit in the group. "You get the others. That's if you know how, street cissy." He disappeared into the darkness.

Beatrice hesitated, thinking of the baby rabbit she had rescued earlier but Belladonna's ugly markings bristled with the excitement of the kill. Her limbs twitched, her whiskers tingled, her mouth watered and her empty belly raged. Beatrice held tight but it was like fighting the wild wind. Just as she felt she would be blown apart in the struggle, something large and leggy dropped from the trees and knocked her over.

"Beatrizia! Ees you? I 'ardly recognise you, but ze spydinis, zey told me you were coming."

"Rico!" She felt her eyes prickle with tears. "It is you, really?"

"Oo else would it be, Piccolina? Though I 'ave to say you 'ave changed a little since I seen you last. And what 'as 'appened to your voice?"

"A long story Rico, you great long-legged furry fairy." Beatrice stepped back in embarrassment. "Oh, I'm so sorry Rico, that was my friend Belladonna. I'm afraid she's a bit well, plain speaking."

"Plain faced and plain speaking, that's me," Belladonna interrupted. "Now let's stop this fancy cat chat and go get Gangsta. Can't let 'im 'ave all the fun."

Beatrice was mortified. "Rico, I'm so sorry, you will get used to her. I have, more or less. She can quite useful

225

sometimes. What she meant, what *I* mean, is let's go and save the rabbits."

"Never fear, Rico is 'ere. And Rico likes a woman with passion, eh my Bella Donna?" Maverico pronounced her name as two words, with relish. "In any case, the matter is – 'ow do you say? – in the hand? I think Señor Gangsta will be back very shortly. Aah, 'ere 'e is now with my friend, Frederico."

Out of the gloom came a rangy dog fox. His yellow eyes gleamed and from his jaws hung a limp black rag, shaped like a cat. Blood dripped onto the mossy path.

"Gangsta, is that you, you great gormless lump?" Belladonna sniggered delightedly. "You been caught? Them rabbits knock you out did they? Or did you just decide to hang out with a fox for fun? Mind you don't stain that nice woodland carpet now with all that blood!"

"She ees a 'arsh woman, zis Bella Donna." Maverico's eyes twinkled. "But she is a powerful lady no? I like to dance ze flamenco with 'er one day." He began to waggle his hips and walk sideways suggestively.

Beatrice decided she needed to reassert herself before things got completely out of control. "Not just now Rico, we have other matters to take care of." She turned to Gangsta, dangling dismally from the fox's mouth. "I am sorry for you, Gangsta, but as you see things are about to change around here. Rico, this fox – Frederico – he's not going to kill him, is he?"

"Eees alright Piccolina. Freddy 'ere, 'e is very gentle. And anyway, ze spyders, zey will sort it. Ze spydernets like you wear, zey are not ze only spyder magic. Zees threads, they also can stop ze bleeding. Señor Gangsta, 'e will not be 'armed!"

The fox put Gangsta down on the ground and stood over him, his tongue hanging out. He kept one dirty paw on Gangsta's wounded belly for safety. "He will be alright," he said. "But I am afraid your rabbit friend was not so lucky. I was too late to save him."

"Oh dear," said Beatrice. "Was it anyone we know?"

"Eet was ze Daddy rabbit of ze baby you rescued," said Maverico. "'E insisted on being – 'ow you say? – ze Decoy Duck. 'E wanted to say thank you to you, to do something to 'elp save ze Wildwoods.

"To me 'e is ze 'ero rabbit. Ze martyr, no? 'E said that if 'e died I 'ad to make sure you eat 'im up good and proper. So as 'e can give you something back for what you did for 'im, Piccolina."

Beatrice was touched but the hungry part of her was just a teeny bit disappointed. She could not bring herself to eat a hero, even if he did happen to be a rabbit.

"Maybe we'll take him back for Rufus," she said. "He needs a meal more than we do."

"Not sure about that," said a familiar voice from inside her. "No point being precious about it, I say. Bit of 'ero blood would be good for us. Set us up good and proper."

"Oh do shut up, Bella." Beatrice could feel her lighter side turning darker by the minute. "Anyhow," she said, loftily, "I thought street cats thrived on hunger. Wasn't that what you told Candy?"

She turned to the fox. "Freddy, will you take Gangsta here to Darius so they can patch him up? And then I need you to keep him safe till we have sorted out the other two."

"No need, no need," came a twinkly voice from above. "Spambulance service is already here, thanks to the spydinis."

"Oh, hello Darius! And the rest of you." Beatrice eyed the scores of spyders letting themselves slowly down from the trees on their fine threads. "Well, that means we can leave Gangsta with you then. Now come on Rico and bring that poor rabbit. And where are all these reinforcements Jake talked about? We need to get organised."

Maverico looked a bit shamefaced. "Ees 'arder to find than I thought. Ze bats, zey are sleeping. And ze squirrels, you cannot rely on. Zey are interested only in ze nuts. Ouch!" He rubbed his head. "What was that? Ow!" A volley of ammunition was coming from somewhere above them.

The next stone hit Beatrice so hard it cut her head open. A horrible cackling came from on high. She glanced up, her paws shielding her face, to where armies of squirrels filled the bare branches. Why had she not noticed them coming? And why hadn't the wonderful spydinis picked them up through the wood-wide web for that matter? But there was not much time to think. The missiles were coming thick and fast. Some of the squirrels hung upside down by their tails, others swung from branch to branch. Some hurled their pebbles from within the hollows of the great beech trees, others from the clefts in the tree trunks left by fallen branches. The attack was wild but appeared coordinated and accompanied by shouts and shrieks.

"Suffrage for squirrels!"

"Woods for the Wild Ones!"

"Nameless and shameless!"

The squirrels began to chant the last phrase all together, like a war cry. The stones rained down relentlessly, tearing the fine spyder threads to pieces and sending the spyders scuttling in all directions. Maverico and Beatrice ran, dodging this way and that to avoid the fire.

"The Nameless must have got into the squirrels," gasped Beatrice, between attacks. "But Jake never said anything about them being so noisy. Or maybe that bit's just the squirrels themselves eh Rico? Rico?"

But there was no reply. Maverico lay unmoving on the ground. Beatrice nudged him with her nose. Then she licked his face. He must have been hit by one of the missiles, but he was alive. She could feel his faint breath against her cheek. She looked around for the old dog fox. "Freddy, where are you? Rico needs help."

228

Freddy was hiding inside the split trunk of a dead oak tree. Cautiously he poked his nose out and padded across the conflict zone to where Rico lay.

"Please Freddy, can you carry him? I need you to take him somewhere safe," said Beatrice. Freddy was about to reply when Belladonna interrupted.

"Yeah, take him back where you came from, you coward. Hidin' away in a bloomin' tree! Bloomin' pacifist are you? Freddy the Fearful Fox!" Her back arched in anger.

"It's called a tactical retreat." Freddy's voice was truculent. "No good to nobody if we get injured are we?"

"Quite right, Freddy," said Beatrice, hastily. "We have to be strategic about this."

Freddy looked a bit puzzled, as well he might, thought Beatrice. How on earth could anyone else made sense of what was coming out of her mouth when she herself had no idea what she was about to say next?

The fox was just gathering Maverico's long limbs up and preparing to lift him when Beatrice spotted a black form darting away into the darkness. In all the excitement they had forgotten one thing. With the spyders scattered, Gangsta had seized his chance and escaped.

CHAPTER 31

THE OWL AND THE PUSSYCAT

It was a long time before the before the chanting subsided and even longer until Beatrice felt certain that the squirrels and their Nameless had gone and she felt safe enough to set off again. She had to find Gangsta before he got back to the labyrinth and alerted The General.

She was alone now except for Belladonna, who kept her company by spitting and snarling in turn. Beatrice found this surprisingly comforting. Her head was bleeding and throbbing, her legs were tired and she felt very weak. She had not eaten for days. She needed all Belladonna's strength and courage just to keep going. Together they ran diagonally this way and that to confuse anyone trying to follow their scent trail. But after hours of running and searching and sniffing there was still no sign of Gangsta – or Jake and King Billy for that matter. All Beatrice had managed to do was to confuse herself. She was lost again.

* * *

"Psst, Beatrice, in here!" The friendly, stripy face of a badger peeked out from a hole in the rocks. Beatrice headed towards it gratefully.

"Thank you so much."

"No problem, Your Highness. King Billy told me to keep an eye out for you. The name is Betsy."

"Oh, that's good," said Beatrice, relieved. "At least you've got a name."

"I do indeed, praise be to the woods." Betsy bowed her head reverently, then smiled. "And so have you – names, I mean. Plenty from what I've heard. Or more than enough to be going on with anyway. Still, Beatrice will do for now, don't you think?" Beatrice nodded agreement, though she could feel Belladonna ready to voice her own opinion on the matter at any moment.

"But you must be hungry," Betsy continued. "Can I interest you in a vole? Or a few earthworms perhaps?"

"A vole would be lovely." Hungry as she was Beatrice still could not imagine eating worms. So the big badger and the little cat huddled down together and tucked into their tea. Betsy just ate the worms and a few mushrooms. Beatrice ate one vole, then another and finished off with a tasty field mouse. Never had food tasted so magnificent.

"I don't suppose you have heard how Candy is, have you?" she asked when she had finally finished eating and taken a moment or two for a quick wash.

"From what I know, she's fine." The badger was busily cleaning out dead leaves and bracken from her den before taking it outside to air. "She came to OK after Sheba licked her into shape. Well, you wouldn't dare do anything less with Sheba, would you? She's worried about you though."

"What about the others? Jake and Rufus? Are they alright?"

"Well, I understand Jake's got Grubsta under control. Of course old Grub can't tell The General what's happened anyway, having no tongue. And with that iron leg The General can't manage to get through that passage to check on Candy himself. So Grub's going back and fore just like always, only Jake gets to eat whatever rations he brings. Which suits him, as you can imagine." Beatrice grinned. "And King Billy is making special deliveries for Rufus too, which Jake takes down to him. But he's very poorly still. And of course Maverico is still out for the count."

"So what happens next?"

"That's difficult. The original plan was to capture Gangsta and then for Maverico to lead the charge on The General. But of course everything's changed now. Gangsta's escaped and Maverico's unconscious. I don't know what they're going to do." She shook her big head from side to side.

Beatrice stood up. She had not actually intended to stand, but Betsy's words had woken Belladonna who was wriggling and twitching furiously so that Beatrice was unable to control her legs. They jerked and jumped around at will. She opened her mouth, intending to apologise, but it was Belladonna who spoke.

"Well if those guys have given up, I'll just 'ave to do it myself. Call themselves military experts. A bit of cunning, that's what they need, none of this strategy lark. I need to go. NOW!"

Betsy flexed her huge front claws. "I'll come with you."

"Nice idea missus, but you're too big." Belladonna was dismissive. "Great lumbering thing. You'll attract attention."

Betsy looked hurt. "I may be big but I'm actually quite fast."

"That is to say, thank you very much for your kind offer," Beatrice interjected. "What we meant to say was that we know you badgers are renowned as warriors, but I think we might be less conspicuous alone. And Betsy, if you get the chance, will you tell Jake we're on our way?"

Beatrice set off hastily, before Belladonna could cause any more trouble, wondering as she went just when she had begun to refer to herself as "we" and what exactly it meant.

* * *

Out in the woods all was quiet. Beatrice crept carefully along, hiding behind fallen tree trunks and checking constantly for smells, sounds or sightings that could indicate the presence of the Nameless. This was difficult because the Nameless were apparently invisible until they took someone over, as they had done with the squirrels. Till then she had no idea where they were. They might be on her shoulder now, just waiting for an opportunity to pounce, or around the next corner. Beatrice hoped she would be safe from possession because, as Jake had pointed out, she had already given her Nameless a name in Belladonna. But was that enough? And who else could she trust?

It occurred to her that without Belladonna for company she would have felt very alone. Who could have imagined that the hard, ugly street kitten could actually become a comfort? Bella was embarrassing and rude and often quite horrible, but she was also tough and brave and fearless and sometimes very funny. Sometimes she just said the things Beatrice was thinking and didn't dare to say out loud. Belladonna did not care what anybody thought. It was like having a living, breathing suit of armour. And right now Beatrice was very glad of her.

"Now, my dear, you don't get away so easily."

Something in the voice set Beatrice's tail a-quiver. A big hairy paw landed on her shoulder and she found herself looking directly into Betsy's face once more. Except that this face was not the sweet, smiling one she had been talking to just a few minutes earlier. This Betsy wore a ferocious grin and her eyes glittered demonically. The powerful jaws displayed rows of sharp teeth. The badger grabbed Beatrice with her claws and dangled her in the air before dropping her hard on the earth.

"Snotty little spy-cat! Not good enough to come along with you just now, was I? Too big? Too – what was the word…lumbering? As you see, I'm big enough and fast enough to catch you aren't I, Mrs high-and-mighty Princess-with-a-thousand-names.

"Well, just cos you're ugly and stupid don't think I don't know what you're about. And The General will pay handsomely for your return."

233

Beatrice gazed into the wild hate-filled eyes. So this was how it worked. Had the Nameless been hiding inside Betsy all the time, or had they swooped the moment Beatrice had left? She tried to look past the hatred to the gentle badger she had been talking to earlier. The one who had gladly given up her last vole so that Beatrice could eat. But it was like trying to see through the fog all over again. The old Betsy had disappeared. Beatrice felt suddenly tiny and terrified. Then, all of a sudden, a wave of something fierce and brave and furious swept through her.

"Ok Bee, I got this!"

The next moment Belladonna swiped Betsy right across the face. Her sharp claws cut into the badger's sensitive nose. Betsy howled with pain. Belladonna struck again, drawing her claws right down Betsy's snout. This time she drew blood. Betsy's howls became a roar. Belladonna gave one last vicious swipe then turned and ran. Beatrice held her breath as they raced through the dead bracken, over the tree stumps and in and out of the grey boulders with the crazed badger hard on their heels. She had no idea where they were going. The big animal got closer and closer till Beatrice could feel its breath on her rump. The badger's doggy scent was in their nostrils. They would not be able to make it as far as the next tree, even if they could be sure the squirrels and the Nameless were not hiding there. For the first time Beatrice felt a desperation in Belladonna. And then, when all seemed lost, a hissing sound came from the undergrowth.

"S…S…Siss…ssters…s…s! This way!"

Beneath a pile of dead leaves Beatrice glimpsed the red eye of a snake. She felt Bella's hesitation. Could they trust it? Did they have a choice?

"It's OK, Bella," she whispered, "Do as he says."

For once Belladonna obeyed without argument. She swerved quickly into the undergrowth just as the snake

234

slithered into the path of the pursuing badger. Betsy, whose eyesight was poor like all badgers, tripped right over him. Instantly the snake's forked tongue darted out and stung her hard on the hindquarters. The badger squealed and turned but the snake was faster. This time he got her in the chest. Beatrice winced but Belladonna thrilled with excitement. The badger tried to stand and face her assailant, but her legs gave way. The snake bit her again and again until poor Betsy's bottom was all swollen and she was beside herself with pain.

"Do stop, do stop!" Beatrice pleaded, unable to bear the cruelty any longer. The snake paused and reared up, turning its head to look at her. Its forked tongue licked the air, while the badger writhed in pain on the ground.

"Thank you for your help, of course. I don't know what we would have done without you." Beatrice was expecting Belladonna to interrupt at any moment, but she was unusually silent.

"You see, it's not Betsy's fault," Beatrice continued, "It's... well I don't know their name, of course, because they are Nameless. Anyway, they are the ones we should be fighting, not Betsy.

"But I do know you who you are, I think. And I know your name. You are Cedric. Or maybe a smaller version of him? Perhaps a cousin? How did you get here?"

"S...s...s...sort of." The snake's head circled continuously as he spoke. It made Beatrice feel a bit dizzy. "We are all C...C...C...Cedrics. We are One. In your s...s...service, of course. We heard our Mas...s...ster call and we mus...s...st obey. There is...s...s no s...s...s...sea in the woods...s...s and no s...s...swamp, so we s...s...suffice..." The snake turned his head this way and that as though searching for other Cedrics all around. "We are watching. Now go...."

"But what shall we do about Betsy?" asked Beatrice. The

wounded badger had stopped squealing now and appeared to have lost consciousness.

"Never fear. The s…s…spyders will…s…s…see to her. She will be s…s…s…safe. Now s…s…so long my princess… ss…ss."

* * *

Beatrice's legs trembled as she continued her journey, searching for any sign of Nameless badgers or foxes or squirrels or frogs or rabbits or even worms. She had begun to realise that she could look and listen and sniff as much as she liked, but it might not do any good. The Nameless did not move with their own bodies or speak with their own voices.

She had not gone far when the air around her became very still. Nothing moved on the land or in the sky. Not the trees, nor the clouds, nor any living creature. Instead there was a queer sort of silence, as though something had sucked all the sound out of the world and all the life at the same time. Beatrice felt a freezing fear take hold of her. She crouched down as a shadow crossed the moon, casting the woods into sudden darkness. A moment later sharp talons gripped her spine and the ground beneath her paws disappeared as she was lifted up higher and higher, through the trees and into the sky.

She looked up at the broad, still wings of the huge owl who had hold of her. It flew with hardly a movement, just an occasional graceful, slow beat. She could just see its great round head, like a dark moon, and its cruel, hooked beak. So this was what it felt like to fly. She should have been frightened but then she heard Belladonna whooping with delight, as though each new swoop was a thrilling game, as though she had been riding the skies for years.

Beatrice looked down at the Wildwoods. Suddenly they looked rather small and not wild at all, like a young animal that needed protecting. Everything seemed distant and unreal. The strange silence that had filled the woods persisted for a few minutes. And then the cries began. They came from the earth and the rocks and the trees and the branches. One by one they rose and joined together in the darkness like a terrible orchestra. Rabbits screamed, squirrels chuntered and foxes howled. The spyders sighed, the badgers grunted and the barn owls screeched. Above them all she heard a long single note, so sharp and poignant that it cut right through her spydernet, and made her bones shiver and her heart break. It was an unfamiliar sound and yet she recognised it immediately. It was the sound of Sheba, calling. A sound so terrible and so raw that it caused the very air and the earth to tremble.

That was the moment when Beatrice realised she was about to die.

* * *

The owl circled above the trees several times, as though enjoying the furore, before settling at the top of a huge oak. Its nest was lined with brown pellets and bits of fur and bone. Below them the noises had changed from sadness and despair into all out warfare. The squirrels were squealing and chattering and throwing more stones. The foxes and the badgers were fighting amongst themselves. The woods echoed with shrieks and barks and grunts and howls. Then, in a clearing below, Beatrice glimpsed the head of a magnificent stag. His antlers gleamed mother of pearl in the moonlight. Could that be Lord Frank? Would he be able to save them?

The owl put Beatrice down amid all the twigs and dead things, keeping one talon firmly on her shoulder. Then it swivelled its head right round and looked directly at her. Its eyes reminded her of the glass marbles she had sometimes played with in the attic. They were cold and clear with huge black centres. And empty. Completely empty. This must be where the Nameless were hiding, whoever they were.

She stared, entranced, unable to tear her gaze away. There was nothing to see and yet with each second she felt she was looking deeper into the darkness. Or walking further and further into a tunnel with no end. As she went deeper she began to hear them and see them and feel them, though not in the ways she usually saw or heard or felt things. They did not exist, they were not real, they had no shape, no name. Yet she knew them and so did Belladonna.

Could she hear a faint muttering? See a slight movement? Darkness stirring within darkness. Or perhaps it was just a memory. But, if so, whose? Whose were these feelings which had festered underground, brooding and breeding and were now about to be unleashed like a plague on the Wildwoods. A kick here or a cruel taunt there, the dislike growing to hatred, the slight, nurtured and cultivated into murderous revenge. Bitterness and resentment, loneliness and despair, the yawning chasms of self-hatred, the chilly wastelands of indifference.

She gazed, fascinated and fearful at the same time. Who knew darkness could be so glittering and so hollow, so black and so unending? Who knew it could take so many forms and still remain invisible? That it could fill your lungs so you could not breathe. That it could draw you in so deep that you could not see yourself or the beautiful world around you. Or that you might not care.

Belladonna was drawn to the darkness like a magnet. Beatrice could feel her slipping away and sense her powerful desire. For what? To be absorbed. To be annihilated. To be one with the ever darkening darkness. She tried to pull her back, grabbing at herself with her claws but to no avail. Belladonna fought hard, tugging and scramming and biting to get free till Beatrice felt she was being ripped apart – that her markings would break free completely and disappear into the owl's eyes and leaving only her own naked, beating heart.

She stopped struggling and tried to think of beauty and goodness and nobility, as Sheba had taught her, but they were all too vague and it was hard to focus with the darkness filling her mind. So instead she thought about Jake and Maverico and Rufus and Cedric and Dino and Myrtle and all the lovely creatures she had met and knew by name. And then she thought of Belladonna herself with her courage and her quick wit and her powerful anger that could make Beatrice feel safe inside. And suddenly, she knew what to do.

"Belladonna," she called softly. And then a little louder, "Belladonna, Belladonna."

At first Belladonna seemed puzzled, unable to understand why Beatrice was not fighting back. It was hard to continue a battle when there was no foe. The darkness continued to call her to itself in its own wordless tongue. But now Beatrice was calling her too. Softly and gently. And now it was Belladonna, not Beatrice who was being pulled in different directions.

Beatrice continued her chant, repeating Belladonna's name over and over until it became a song with a rhythm and a life all of its own. Into her song Beatrice poured all the joy and beauty and love she had ever felt in her short life. Love for Jake and the muscateers, for Candy, for the clouds and the sky and the Fall, for Dino and Cedric and the spyders, for Jack Daw, for the woodland with all its wonderful creatures, and even for Sheba. Now that love was all wrapped up in a single name. Belladonna. Belladonna. Belladonna. The love became so strong that Beatrice forgot her fear of The General and the Nameless. She even forgot her fear of losing Belladonna. And then she felt her dark, angry markings begin to soften and she knew it had worked. Belladonna was giving up the struggle. She was surrendering, coming back, back to Beatrice where she belonged. Beatrice opened her heart and enveloped her with love so powerful Belladonna began gasping for air.

"Easy does it Bee," she growled. "I'm suffocatin' 'ere. You've made your point. I'm not going nowhere."

No you are not, thought Beatrice. Not nowhere. Sometimes bad grammar was better at telling the truth than proper sentences, whatever Sheba might say.

Then the owl opened its beak and let out a screech so full of despair that Beatrice, whose heart was still full of love for Belladonna, felt overwhelmed with compassion. Her newly restored companion, though, had no such compunction and was already back on the case.

"You! Owl! Call yourself wise?" Belladonna growled. "Pretty stupid to allow yourself to be taken over like that. Too stupid to remember your own name. And now so stupid you're going to eat the one person who might help you. Or maybe the two people. Well you don't frighten me. Or us."

But the Nameless Owl had already begun tearing at Beatrice with his beak, pulling out her fur, muttering furiously to itself the whole time.

Fur and bone.
Sticks and stone.
Spit them out.
Make them moan.

Beatrice felt his beak ripping her flesh apart and heard herself scream, as though from very far away. Then Belladonna was fighting back furiously, yelling and swearing and scratching for all she was worth, so that the noise in the nest drowned out even the sounds of the battlefields below. The moon came out from behind the clouds and in the silvery light Beatrice saw that the owl's face was bleeding. And then, out of the corner of her eye, she saw something else. Something so strange and so magical that for an instant she forgot about the owl and Belladonna and her own pain and even the possibility that she was about to be eaten alive.

It was shaped like a triangle but it seemed to be made up of thousands of separate sections which moved as one and swept across the skies with an effortless grace. The creature lifted and swooped and folded upon itself, its every movement a work of art. One minute it flew like an arrow, the next it waved like a flag, furling and unfurling in the night air. It twisted and turned and dived and soared. It wound itself into a tight ball and stretched itself out like a scarf. Then it drew itself together into a V shape and flew straight towards them, just as the owl was about to take a big chunk from Beatrice's belly.

The owl's beak opened in surprise. Beatrice ducked down into the nest to avoid being hit by the magnificent creature. But at the last minute it reared away and then it seemed to separate and fall apart. Suddenly the nest was full of black feathers flapping and black beaks snapping. The owl swept his wings forwards and backwards furiously as he tried to fend off the many-headed, multi-winged creature. Then, over the din of fighting and flapping, she heard a familiar voice.

"You, George! Get your thievin' talons offa my girl."

Jack Daw was sitting on top of the owl's head, his talons gripping its skull, his beak pecking hard at the owl's flat face. Around him a halo of other birds hovered, wings a-flutter.

"'Scuse the dramatic entrance, Madam. Always wanted to do that. My friends, the starlings 'ere, they said I could lead the murmuration. Just till we got 'ere like." He leaned over the top of the owl's head. "And if you don't stop that behaviour an' give this young lady back to me I'll 'ave 'em all in 'ere. An' they'll peck those creepy eyes out and swivel that silly 'ead round and round until it unscrews. An' if that's not enough," he looked at Beatrice triumphantly, "I have the rooks at the ready."

CHAPTER 32

THE WOOD AT WAR

On Jack Daw's cue the rooks took off from the surrounding trees and swirled around, squawking and screeching. Beatrice found herself in the middle of a huge spiral of sound. At first she found it hard to work out what they were saying as they were all shouting over each other. But eventually she understood. This murderous owl was the very same one that had eaten her angry words when she had come across Sheba and Candy together on her first night out in the woods with Jake. That all seemed very far away now. But this owl was indeed wise old George – or it had been before he had been invaded by the Nameless. And now the rooks were calling him back.

"George, George, George!"

Their squawks echoed out over the woodland and bounced back from the rock faces. The noise was so intense that it almost drowned out the battle cries below.

"Now it's your turn missus," Jack Daw said, in between pecks at the owl's head. "It's you 'e's 'avin' a go at, after all. Well, it's not actually George 'avin' a go at you, of course. It's this 'ere Nameless inside of 'im. Made 'im forget 'imself. So you gotta remind 'im. Bit like you did just now with what's 'er name. Belladonna." He cackled. "Oh yes, we was watching you, luv. Very impressive. So you just start off an' we'll back you up if you need it."

Beatrice was hesitant, fearful of what she might see if she looked again into the owl's eyes again.

"Don't worry, luv," Jack Daw croaked. "Just be yourself, an 'e'll be 'imself. Least, that's the way I think it works."

The rooks fell silent. The noises of the battle below them faded away. Beatrice slowly lifted her gaze. With her new friends around her the huge eyes which met hers no longer seemed so scary. They were just empty, like a big dark hole waiting to be filled.

"Go on luv," Jack Daw's voice was gentle. "'E needs you, you know."

Beatrice had not thought of the situation that way. She found it surprisingly helpful. "George?" she said, hesitantly. There was no response so she tried a bit louder. "George? That's your name, isn't it? Is that you in there? I'm Princess Beatrice and I'm delighted to meet you. Please, talk to me."

The owl stared back at her, vacantly. She looked across at Jack Daw. He in turn looked around at the rooks perched in the branches all around.

"Right, come on lads, let's give the lady an 'and. Best dawn chorus voices now. On my count. One, two three…"

"George!" the rooks cawed, all together. The noise was deafening. They shouted the name over and over till Beatrice had to put her paws over her ears to block out the sound.

Jack Daw interrupted. "OK, that's enough boys. Time for the lady to try a softer approach again, I think. Bad cop, good cop an' all that."

Beatrice waited for the last of the caws to die away and then she waited a bit longer still, till the air had stopped re-verberating and she felt quiet inside.

This time she whispered. "George? George, I know you are in there somewhere. Please come back. We need you. The Wildwoods need you. I need you."

There was a moment, which seemed to go on forever, when nothing happened. And then George blinked, ever so slowly, like someone waking from a deep sleep. She looked again into his eyes and saw that the dreadful black holes which had nearly sucked Belladonna in were now glossy dark lakes, deep and still and calm. Beatrice felt herself reflected in them, filled with love and gentleness. She could hear the shrieks and howls of warfare coming from the woods below but she could not imagine fighting anyone. She could hardly even imagine Belladonna. A moment of panic gripped her. She couldn't lose Belladonna. Not now. Not yet.

"'Old your 'orses, luv. I'm not goin' nowhere." She was relieved to hear Belladonna's voice in her ear. "Though I 'ave to say that was all a bit softly softly for my taste. But you an' me an' George. I reckon we're a winning team. What d'you say?"

Beatrice felt Belladonna's courage and determination sweep through her once more and with them another sensation that was harder to identify – a sense of completeness, of being whole, of coming home.

"You and me, Bella, we're the real team," she whispered.

George lifted his head and gave a long, low hoot, so pure in its tone that Beatrice felt shivers running up and down her spine.

"Right, well, I'm glad we got that sorted out." Jack Daw stepped off George's head and began to preen himself. "Nice to 'ave you back, George."

"Delighted, I'm sure," George replied in soft, modulated tones. "And so deeply sorry if I have inadvertently caused offence or inconvenienced you in any way while I was, er, indisposed."

"Don't worry, George, we know it wasn't really you." Beatrice still thought it was a good idea to use George's name at every opportunity. You could never be too careful. "But where've they gone, those Nameless creatures? And what if they come back?"

"Oh they'll be off looking for someone else to occupy themselves with," said Jack Daw nonchalantly. "Old George will be alright now. Long as 'e remembers 'is true name and

244

we remember 'is true name they won't be back. Jus' some-times, we all forget ourselves and then we're in trouble. That's why we all need each other, see? To remember, like. I'll remember who you are if you remember me."

The owl swivelled his head to look over at Jack Daw. His big black eyes were smiling.

"Oh, I'll remember you alright, Mr Daw. Until today I thought it was we owls who were meant to be the wise ones." He hooted softly with laughter.

Jack Daw cackled. "Less of the Mister. You'd better just call me Jack or I won't know who you're talking to. Don't answer to Mister, I'm afraid. But right now my wisdom tells me we have to get moving after old Gangsta or this murmuration of starlings will become a squawkuration. Thanks, guys."

The starlings did a little loop-the-loop in acknowledgement.

"Might I make a suggestion?" said George, tentatively. He still seemed a bit bewildered by the night's events. "If I give a lift to our friends here, then we could travel faster and avoid the squirrels."

Beatrice was amused to hear him including Belladonna separately in his invitation.

"Good idea," she replied, "but, please, watch where you are putting your claws this time."

Her head still hurt from the squirrel stoning. Her back was bleeding where George's talons had dug into her and there was a big bare patch on her belly, where he had pulled out her fur.

"I am so sorry." George shook his head slowly from side to side. "I would never have hurt you intentionally, your Royal Highness. Though I am not quite sure about that other one you have with you. Your friend. She's a rather, ahem, different story." He winked, which looked very strange in an owl.

"Shut your big beak up Georgie Porgie! It's a much more interesting story with me in it, that's for sure," muttered Belladonna. "And at least I'm not a traitor!"

"Oh, do stop it Bella. He's only teasing," said Beatrice, hurriedly. "And please don't worry, George. But how do you know…Oh, my goodness!" Beatrice had just noticed something. The owl's sharp claws had not just torn out her fur. They had also ripped through the spydernet. And something was happening to her markings. The ones on the underside were beginning to move.

Her head and spine and tail were still irredeemably ugly. But her chest and paws and belly were beginning to look quite pretty and the markings were arranging themselves so that they neatly covered the bare patch that had been there just moments earlier. She recognised the familiar wriggly sensation as they adjusted themselves and then the wonderful comfortable feeling as the colours settled into position. For the first time since Darius had spun her spydernet she felt free, as though somebody had undone her shackles. And then she felt guilty. Did Belladonna know? What would she say when she found out? But there was no time to think about it properly. Jack Daw was getting ready to depart.

"Come on you lot. Let's be 'avin' you. Time for take-off."

The starlings took their places in formation behind Jack Daw. George spread his wings and glided ever so gently away from the nest, with Beatrice hanging beneath. Jack Daw and the starlings followed, turning and swooping and twisting and looping like a single giant bird against the pale skies of early dawn. And all around the air filled with unruly flapping as scores of rooks took off from the surrounding trees.

This time Beatrice found herself enjoying flying almost as much as Belladonna. George was silent now, totally focused. She thought about the owl's glossy eyes with their dark, bottomless centres and imagined being inside them, looking out. Then, just for a moment, it was as though she was really there, seeing the world as George saw it. The tiniest details became crystal clear. She could make out individual blades of grass and the textures of dead leaves. She spotted field mice and woodlice and even the spydinis. It was a strange experience, being inside George's head, and it only lasted for an instant but it reminded Beatrice of the way the world changed when she looked at it through Belladonna's eyes. Then she remembered how it felt to be the cape in the Paso Doblé, when she had surrendered completely, to be lifted and folded and waved at will as though she herself was nothing at all, just a movement of air. So many ways of being and seeing. Which one was right? Or were they all true in their various ways?

"There he is!" George's deep voice cut through her reveries. "By those rocks."

Jack Daw, the starlings and the owl turned together and swept downwards, followed by the rooks. Beneath her, Beatrice saw Freddy at the head of a pack of foxes. It was hard to tell at first if he was leading them or being chased by them. And then she spied Gangsta, bleeding and lame, looking up with his one eye at the birds approaching from the sky and then behind at the foxes chasing him. George swooped down so fast that Beatrice's belly nearly ended up in her throat. And then Gangsta was running in front of them while they glided behind, just a few feet above ground.

George took his time, enjoying the chase, picking his moment with precision. Beatrice felt his claws open and the next second she was dropping through the air. She landed directly on top of Gangsta. He was tired by now and badly injured. Beatrice actually felt quite sorry for him, but Belladonna was merciless. She bit and spat and clawed and scratched with a passion and an expertise that still surprised and shocked Beatrice. Where had she learnt those skills? Certainly not from playing in the attic. How could this creature be a part of Beatrice and yet so separate? And what on earth would Sheba make of her?

Above them, George circled serenely, while the starlings, still in perfect formation, swirled and swooped threateningly. The rooks, not so disciplined, were enjoying the fight. Their beady eyes glittered and their black beaks opened and closed frantically as they yelled their support.

"Go at it Beatrice!"

"One eye's too many I say. Take it away!"

"Go for the throat, that's the best bit. Delicious!" yelled one particularly scruffy fellow, bouncing up and down on his branch in excitement.

Gangsta's jugular was open and inviting. Beatrice felt Belladonna's blood in her veins, pulsing wildly with the prospect of the kill and was mortified to find her jaws drooling. Gangsta's single eye stared up at her, wild with terror. Suddenly, his gaze cleared and a look of amazement crossed his face.

"B…Beatrice?" he stammered. "Is it really you, in disguise all this time? Have mercy Beatrice! Mercy!"

Beatrice had been in something of a trance, overwhelmed by Belladonna's fighting skills. But at the mention of her name, she came to sharply. This violence had to be stopped.

"Belladonna! Listen to me Belladonna! Stop this now. You are behaving like the Nameless. You have a perfectly good name. Or a perfectly bad one. Either way, you have no excuse. I command you to stop." She was surprised at how regal she sounded, almost like the great Sheba herself.

Belladonna was not happy. Beatrice could sense her resistance, the muscles straining, the murderous desire to pounce, to bite, to kill, to eat the flesh and drink the blood. But this time Beatrice remained calm and in control. She would not argue. She would simply focus. The spydernet had been breached. Belladonna no longer had the upper hand. She felt her markings thrashing about, writhing, fighting with each other for supremacy. And then, bit by bit, she felt them relax, become soft and yielding as they slid gently back into position, from her belly up to her heart and her head and then right along her spine so she was almost completely herself again – whoever that might be, she thought, wryly. But it was a lovely, cosy feeling, like settling into a comfy old armchair. Gangsta had already given in and now the brave, fierce, cunning, cruel, ugly kitten that was Belladonna was surrendering too and she could be properly Beatrice again – though an irritated scrabbling in her belly told her that Belladonna was still there, somewhere inside and did not intend to take this defeat lying down.

"Good girl, Bella," she murmured and felt a sharp pain as though someone had kicked her hard from inside. "I mean, bad girl. Oh, you know what I mean," she giggled. "You did a great job, you know, I'm so proud of you." The wriggling and kicking subsided. She looked around.

"Now then, if someone could alert the spyders and Sergeant Pepper then perhaps they could tie this chap up again. We have to be getting along to The General."

"No need, no need!" the tinkling voices came from all around her.

"Of course, you already know all about it." Beatrice smiled. "I should have guessed your spies would be out. And could you put some webbing on his wounds too, to stop them bleeding so badly? I'm afraid Belladonna has got a nasty bite."

She turned to the pack of foxes, who had only just caught up with them. "Freddy, thank you so much. Now, would you hold him while the spyders work and make sure he doesn't escape again before he's tied up good and proper?"

Freddy nodded, breathless after the chase. He placed two large paws on Gangsta's belly. "Not going to let him go again, Your Highness," he gasped.

Beatrice looked up at the big owl, perched on a beech branch. "Ready, George?"

The owl sailed down through the bare trees, picked Beatrice up in one smooth movement and headed back into the pale sky. She looked down at her chaotic Queendom, still loud with the cries of war and thick with the crazy shrieks and howls of the Nameless. Where in this madness were her friends, Jake and Maverico and Rufus?

And then she spied someone standing on top of a rock. She had not noticed him at first because he was almost hidden by the large, lumpy creature lying next to him. But, now they were nearer, those long legs were unmistakeable.

"Rico!" she shouted joyfully. "Quick, George, down again!"

Maverico looked up as they approached and gave a deep bow, followed by a quite unnecessary flourish of his paws.

"Ecco! Mia Principessa! And bellissima as ever!"

Beatrice ran up to him delightedly. "Rico, you're better! How did that happen? And what are you doing here?"

"Marvellous Maverico is preparing 'is army, my princess. And see 'ere I 'ave my beautiful war 'orse." He waved at the creature beside him. Beatrice looked. And looked again. The strange looking war horse was actually a woolly rhino.

"Myrtle! What on earth are you doing here? It's dangerous, you know. And what happened to all that terrible ice? And how on earth did you follow us here?"

"Oh, you know, I have been waiting for the call. For ages. For millennia," Myrtle simpered and looked sideways shyly. Maverico jumped onto her back and began trying out some acrobatics. She giggled with pleasure.

"My lord here was injured and needed me. And maybe because that Tunnel thing was open I could hear him call to me. I could feel his love across all the ages." She sighed meaningfully. "And love, as they say, will always find a way. So I came to wake him from his deep, deep sleep with the kiss of life." She turned her head and gave Maverico a big sloppy lick with her tongue.

250

Beatrice felt suddenly nauseous. "But how did you get here?"

"I travelled through the Time Tunnel with the Cedrics and those others, of course."

"Of course," said Beatrice, who was wondering what else might have come through the Tunnel that she did not yet know about. "I think I've met Cedric. But is Dino here too? How lovely!"

Myrtle looked downcast. "No I'm afraid poor Dino did not survive the Ice Age. He couldn't move fast enough to outrun it, see. And of course he did not have my lovely woolly coat to keep warm." She shook her horned head sadly. "No, it was the other ones we came through with. I forget what they are called."

"That's because they're the Nameless," said Beatrice. "They aren't called anything. I am surprised they didn't get you, Myrtle. Though you can look quite big and fierce so maybe that's why they left you alone."

"Or maybe they just didn't want to be called Myrtle," Belladonna muttered. Beatrice tried to keep a straight face. She felt very sad about Dino. "Poor Dino. He was such a gentle soul."

She flinched as something tiny and winged dropped out of the trees and flew off into the woods. "What was that?"

Around them more and more little creatures were darting away into the darkness.

"Ees ze bats, my Princess. Zey 'ave not deserted us. Zis noise, ze rooks and ze battle, it wakes zem from zeir 'ibernation. So now, I 'ave my army. And I 'ave my war 'orse. We are ready."

Myrtle pawed the ground and shook her head in a menacing manner and Beatrice tried again not to laugh. Being serious was harder now that her markings could move about once more. She could feel a large gold smile spreading of its own accord from whisker to whisker.

"What about Jake?"

"Jake 'as 'is own army. Zey are going to 'ead off ze squirrels and ze other Nameless in ze woods. Me, I am storming ze citadel with my bat-tallion and my Timeless friend 'ere. Are you coming, Piccolina?"

"Try to stop me," said Beatrice, adding as an afterthought, "They are all my own armies after all. And I've got my own trusty steed, eh George?"

George managed to look just the tiniest bit insulted as he blinked back at her. Maverico lowered his long legs to either side of Myrtle's flanks.

"Zere is no time for delay eh? 'Ow you say over 'ere? Tally O!"

And off they set. George carried Beatrice, who was now quite used to flying. She watched Maverico, ahead of her, trying to keep his balance while Myrtle charged onwards, bumping into tree trunks and rocky outcrops on the way. She had forgotten how poor Myrtle's eyesight was.

There seemed to be more fallen tree trunks than Beatrice remembered, but curiously they moved out of Myrtle's way as she approached. Then George swooped lower and Beatrice saw that the tree trunks all had the same bark, beautifully patterned with diamonds and she realised they were not trees at all but mini-Cedrics – an army of serpents who had travelled through time to defend the Wildwoods. And they were lying in wait for the Nameless.

As they rode and flew, the bats dropped in glorious squadrons from the trees. Soon they had formed an enormous army, many thousand strong, all flying in formation, just as the starlings had done.

Beatrice was so busy watching the bats that she did not notice at first the extraordinary things that were happening on the ground below her. But when she finally dragged her gaze back down to earth she was amazed to find that every path, every stone and every crevasse seemed to have come alive.

From hidden clefts, from holes in the earth and in the rock face and from hollows at the base of trees, badgers were emerging. At first the movement seemed haphazard but as George flew higher and her vision grew wider she began to see a pattern. Long black and white lines of badgers fanned out from the centre of the woods to its periphery, like spokes from a wheel. And every line was a battle line. They grabbed squirrels and shook them in their powerful jaws till their necks broke. They pounced on Nameless foxes and wrestled them to the ground. They fought hard and fiercely with those of their own kind who housed the Nameless. They were swift, silent warriors with a power that made Beatrice gasp.

Sitting quite still at the centre of it all, beneath a twisted oak tree, she recognised King Billy, the biggest badger of all. And lying nonchalantly alongside him on his back, belly exposed and legs akimbo, was Jake. Next to him was Grubsta, though Beatrice did not recognise him at first because he was so clean. His white fur glowed and his grey markings gleamed in the dawn light. She shouted and waved but they could not stop because she and George were travelling fast to keep pace with Maverico and his bat-tallions.

The sky was full of flitting forms. The earth was running with badgers and twisting with serpents. The air was electric with whoops and squawks and wails. Beatrice felt something inside her leap for joy and knew it was Belladonna. She was, after all, a creature born for warfare. This was her moment. Then Beatrice heard Maverico's triumphant cry. "'Ere! 'ere, my batty ones. Now ees your time for glory."

On command, one after the other, hundreds and then thousands of bats circled and dived and disappeared completely into the earth. For a few minutes Beatrice was puzzled and then she understood what was happening. The bats had found the spot where Rufus fell and they were dropping, one by one, directly into The General's cave. They were going to drive him out. And King Billy with his army would be waiting for them at the other end. She pictured them swarming in the stinking darkness while The General, without his trusted minions, struggled to escape. She could see him waving his good paw wildly and snapping at them with his teeth as they circled and swooped. She imagined the caves echoing with their twitterings and the furious thumps of The General's iron leg. Would it be enough?

Then she saw Maverico slide himself off Myrtle's back and leap into the hole. She remembered Jake's tale of being lowered down in the spyders' hammock and she hoped Maverico's circus skills would be sufficient for him to land safely. Without her adored rider, Myrtle looked lost and downcast.

"Come on Myrtle," shouted Beatrice, "we'll wait for him at the other end."

George turned obligingly. Within seconds she and George were touching down next to Jake.

"Jake!" Beatrice jumped on top of him from behind. "I won't ask what you are doing here. I've got a fair idea."

"Hey, I thought you was supposed to be a dignified princess these days." Jake rolled over and lifted a large paw to her face. "Either that or a dastardly street-kitten."

"Oh, I can be all things," said Beatrice loftily, wondering as she spoke quite what she meant by that.

"Don't I know it, little Bee." Jake's voice sounded unaccountably sad as he patted his belly.

"But, Jake, where's King Billy? I thought I saw him with you just now. And what on earth has happened to Grubsta? What have you done to him?"

"Oh, Old Bill will be back soon. He's just gone to check on his troops. Seems one of the spokes of his war-wheel has gone out of alignment. Bit OCD, Old Bill, if you ask me. Must have a perfect circle. Even in the middle of a war.

254

"As for Grub here, that's your mother's doing – nothing to do with me. Well, he did say he wanted to come over to our side. Least, that's what I thought he would have said if he had a tongue. So I decided to let old Sheba loose on him, spruce him up a bit. She done quite a good job, I'd say."

"Sheba? But where is she?" Beatrice felt her insides grow cold and small.

"Oh, you'll see her in good time. Meanwhile I think we have work to do."

A few of the spydinis scuttled out of the earth and whispered in Jake's ear. They tickled so much he shook his head and they flew through the air, landing unceremoniously back on the soil.

"Listen! Seems like The General's a-coming now." They could hear some heavy clanking footsteps approaching and a deep voice that panted and gasped between curses.

"Just you wait," it growled. "You'll regret this. They're waiting for me out there you know. Ow! Ooh! Do stop dive-bombing me with those wings. Ouch! OK, OK, I'm going as fast as I can."

Inside the tunnel she heard Maverico's whoops of delight and then a cloud of bats burst from the tunnel entrance and rose into the sky. A few seconds later an iron leg poked through the hole and with a few more painful gasps, the burly figure of The General emerged from the darkness. He blinked as the soft light of the sunrise entered his eyes.

"Been a while since he saw the sun I guess," Jake remarked. "Or breathed fresh air for that matter. Must feel mighty strange being outside. Like someone's shaved all your fur off."

In daylight and away from his stronghold The General looked surprisingly vulnerable, like a blind, newborn kitten – except for his iron leg and the noises that were coming from his mouth which were a peculiar mixture of growls and whimpers. As his eyes adjusted slowly to the dawn he began to take in his surroundings and the creatures around him. When he saw Beatrice he squinted extra hard and stamped his iron leg on the ground in disgust.

"Belladonna! So you are the Princess Beatrice! I knew it was a trick. You were way too ugly for this world."

"Why thank you, kind sir!" The gruff voice took Beatrice by surprise. In the excitement of meeting up with Jake she had almost forgotten about Belladonna. But she was pleased to hear her voice again.

"Traitors, all of you!" The General railed. "You – Jake – serving a dead king that couldn't even manage his queen let alone a kingdom." His eyes fell on Grubsta. "And as for you, I should have cut your heart out instead of your tongue. Look at you! Washed and fluffed and brushed, just like any other lap cat – except they've got tongues of course. Hard to lap without a tongue, eh? Heh, heh!" He chuckled bitterly.

"You are such a fool, Grub. The three of us, we were special. We made our own destiny. We could have ruled forever. Anyway, where is Gangsta? He'll be along to rescue me soon. He's worth a hundred of you."

Jake sniggered. "Gangsta's, well, he's a bit tied up at the minute. Seems like your spyder mates were into counterespionage all along."

The General roared with rage. He jumped on Jake, taking him by surprise, and beat him hard over the head with his iron leg. Jake crumpled to the ground. Beatrice waited, expecting him to give one of his sly winks and get up again as if it were all a big joke. But he lay there unmoving.

"You've killed him!" she howled. "You're a cruel monster and…and I'm going to kill you back."

This time it was Beatrice, not Belladonna, who leapt into action with murderous intent. The General had hurt Jake, her beloved friend. Her first friend. Her best friend. Not to mention what he had done to Rufus. This was Beatrice's battle, not Belladonna's, and she fought it with all her strength and with all her love and with all her hatred, dragging her claws across The General's face and eyes, sinking her teeth deep into his haunches, snarling and screeching till there was no telling which was her and which was Belladonna for they were one, at last. He fought back hard, his stinking yellow fangs tearing into her flesh and ripping it to the bone while his metal leg swung angrily, like a cudgel. Beatrice dodged and weaved and slashed and scratched, ignoring the blood which poured from both of them and mixed together traitorously on the earth. She was fighting for the Queendom and Rufus and Maverico and Candy, but most of all for Jake. *All Four One* she repeated inside with each blow given and received. *All Four One. One Four All.* It didn't work with three. He'd killed everything – everything that mattered. She sprang at him wildly, fearlessly, desperately.

But it was no good. The General was twice her size. As she jumped he twisted to one side, raised his iron leg up and brought it down hard on her shoulders, knocking her onto her back. He was standing over her with his metal fist raised, ready for the final blow, when there was a loud shriek and four long legs wrapped themselves around him from behind.

"En garde, my friend. No one escapes from the Mighty One! And that is no way to treat a lady!" With a flourish, Maverico pulled The General off Beatrice and threw him to the floor.

CHAPTER 33

THE WAY OF THE WARRIOR

"Over 'ere, my trusty steed, my war 'orse. Come, I need you."

Myrtle had been mooning around and sighing meaningfully while Maverico had been in The General's cave but seeing her hero reappear in such a spectacular fashion brightened her up no end. She began to dance her way over to him in a slow rumba fashion, but her legs turned to jelly with all the excitement and she fell over.

"What is it that you desire, my darling, my Master?" she asked when she managed to pick herself up again.

"I need your 'elp to keep zis monster still. Ees best you lie on top of 'im, I think."

"But of course, Master."

Myrtle obediently settled herself down on top of The General. She took pains not to crush him completely but she was nevertheless heavily built and about twenty times his size and he howled indignantly as she adjusted her position. Beatrice could just see his furious face poking out from underneath Myrtle's tummy. After a few minutes the wails changed to a continuous rumbling growl. Jake still lay silent on the ground. Beatrice sat next to him, rubbing his head with her own and licking his closed eyes. What was the point of winning the Wildwoods back if Jake wasn't there to enjoy it with her?

Just then a wraith-like creature stepped from the labyrinth entrance and collapsed in a heap on the ground. "Aaah, there you are! Bit of a rum do that. Sorry I couldn't be more help. Can't move as fast as I could. But better late than never, I suppose."

"Rufus!" Beatrice rushed up to him in delight, then drew back when she saw the ribs jutting out of his gaunt frame. His gold fur was matted and faded. His eyes were closed and his breathing was heavy and short.

"Ah, 'ere 'e ees." Maverico looked up from stroking Myrtle's neck. "I carry 'im nearly all the way until I 'ear you fighting. Zen I 'ave to leave. 'E is very weak – even with ze extra rations ze badgers brought 'im."

"Poor Rufus. What has he done to you!" She turned to The General furiously. "You are a cruel, despicable cat. And mark my words, I am going to rid these woods of you once and for all, even if I have to do it without Rufus and Jake."

"Good to know I can have a bit of a rest then, Sweet Bee. My head sure hurts." Jake had regained consciousness and was sitting up and rubbing his forehead. "And let me tell you General, when she says something in that tone of voice then you can be sure it will Bee, eh Bee?"

"Jake! So you're not dead after all!" Beatrice left Rufus and raced over to him.

"Not when I last looked, Sweet Bee. Though I sure have felt better. But I'm not as bad as poor Roof there."

"But what can we do, Jake?" She lowered her voice to a whisper. "And how do we get rid of The General."

"Kill him!" Belladonna's voice rose unbidden out of Beatrice's throat.

"Quiet Bella, you know that's not the answer," Beatrice said, severely, forgetting that she had been attacking The General herself only minutes earlier. But that had been when she thought Jake was dead. "Killing would make us as bad as him. We need to find somewhere we can we send him to be sure he won't come back."

Jake thought for a bit. "I reckon there's only one place that'll work." He looked suddenly serious. "We have to send him back down the Time Tunnel. He never should have come back out see, once they'd got his leg an' all. Fact is, it suited the Powers Beneath to do the deal so the Nameless could come through with him. But the good news is that if he goes back, I reckon so do they."

"But how do we find it again from here? It seems an age since we were there. And I have no idea where it actually is."

"Reckon the bats will know," said Jake. "But we'll need to do it soon. They're beginning to look sleepy. I reckon they'll need to hibernate again soon."

It was true. The bats had stopped flitting about and were festooning the branches of every available tree, like little bits of brown bunting left over from a party long ago.

"I'm sorry, I couldn't help overhearing." Myrtle's high voice piped up rather hesitantly. "It's just that I know where the Time Tunnel is. I have only just come from there after all."

"Brilliantly said, Carissima! Not just beautiful, but clever, too! You can lead us there." Maverico planted a big kiss on her cheek. Myrtle squirmed with pleasure, which made The General groan and swear even more loudly beneath her.

"I think we should all go together," said Beatrice. "Especially with the war still going on." In all the excitement the cats had become oblivious to the battle cries all around them. Now they sat and listened with grave expressions.

"We'll need a badger escort, I reckon," said Jake.

"Naturally." King Billy had reappeared, puffing slightly from his exertions. "You don't think we are going to miss out on this moment, do you? After all, it's new beginnings for all of us."

"Me too! Me too! Me too!" The squawking of Jack Daw and the starlings and rooks was so loud that for a few minutes it drowned out once more the noise of warfare.

"The more the merrier, I say," Jake grinned. "Let's have a party!"

"As I remember that's what started all this in the first place," said Beatrice tartly.

"If I might make a suggestion?" Sergeant Pepper dropped himself down from an overhanging birch tree. "We can make some shackles for the prisoner, and then we could attach it to an extra strong lead – the sort we used to lower Jake here into the cave. That way he cannot escape as we travel."

"That's a great idea," said Beatrice. "But what will we do about Rufus meanwhile? He's too weak to walk."

At the sound of his name, Rufus opened his eyes. "Please, don't bother yourselves about me," he panted. "I will stay here and await my fate. It is the way of the warrior, after all. And if I die, I am glad to do it in your service, Your Royal Highness."

"Well, it may be the way of the warriors but it's not the way of the muscateers," Beatrice replied, firmly. "We'd never leave you like this, Rufus. *All Four One*, remember?"

"There may come a time when you have to leave me," Rufus's voice was getting weaker. "Or I have to leave you, my Princess."

"No need for that," piped up Myrtle. Reunited with her love, she seemed to be gaining confidence by the minute. "He can ride on my back. It's very broad and woolly and comfortable. And if he gets dizzy he can hold onto my horn. I seem to remember my darling here saying something about vertigo. You don't mind me carrying him do you, my dear?"

"Ees my pleasure, mia amore," said Maverico, magnaminously.

So Myrtle rolled halfway off The General to allow the spyders to begin work on his collar and harness. When they were finished, and The General safely bound, Beatrice and Jake and Maverico carried Rufus over to where she lay. Myrtle knelt down on her front legs and, with a bit of help from the others, Rufus managed to clamber on and lie down flat on her woolly back.

"Ah, lovely, that's much better," he sighed and buried his nose in her soft coat. Myrtle pushed herself upright slowly, careful to keep her precious cargo safely balanced.

And so they set off, with Myrtle leading the way and Rufus lying on top of her. Behind limped The General, led by Beatrice who held one skein of his harness ropes in her mouth. Maverico and Jake were on either side, each also holding a rope. Above flew George, holding a longer skein in his beak. The rooks and the starlings, directed by Jack Daw, formed a protective cloud of wings over them as they walked and the badgers organised themselves into a diamond-shaped posse surrounding them on the ground. Occasionally George forgot how slowly cats and woolly rhinos travelled and flew a bit too fast. When that happened The General's collar tightened and he began to choke so George waited patiently in a tree for them all to catch up. It occurred so often though that Beatrice wondered if George was doing it on purpose. Within no time at all, it seemed, they had arrived at their destination.

"I don't understand," said Beatrice. "It's so near. We must have been going around in circles before." She thought back to the bats' guano map with its confusing spirals.

"That's Time for you," said Jake, knowingly.

"I would have said it was more about space myself," Beatrice replied, rather huffily. "But if you know so much, perhaps you can tell us how we make sure he goes down and stays down."

Jake thought. "I don't think we can go with him this time. For sure we wouldn't be travelling with love would we? Not with him for company. And we've done our bit. But you're right. Someone has to take him right through and stay with him in case the Tunnel decides to spit him back out again. Can't say I'd blame it neither."

There followed a long, heavy silence. The sort where the birds stop singing – or squawking – and the wind stops moving and even the grass stops growing. The silence which descends when there is a question with only one answer and nobody dares to speak it.

"Rico?" said Jake, at last.

But Maverico would not meet his eyes. He looked away into the distance from his throat came a strangled sob. Myrtle stood, staring at the tunnel, Rufus still on her back. She pawed the ground and two huge tears fell from her eyes. Eventually she spoke and her voice was no longer squeaky but low and mellow.

"I know. I know. It has got to be me. My work here is done and I have to go back to my own time. Oh, my love, courage!" She looked over to where Maverico stood gazing into the woodland. "I came for you. For love. That is why I travelled safely. And now I leave for you. For love. For all of you. My greatest joy is to know that you are safe, that I have done my bit to secure the future. No, I lie." She went up to Maverico and nuzzled his hindquarters with her huge head. Rufus slid quietly from her back onto the ground.

"My greatest joy, my love, was to dance with you. And with your glorious cape, too, of course." She glanced over at Beatrice who could hardly see through her own tears. "That was truly a moment out of time. But for me it lasts for all time. Like our love."

Finally, Maverico turned to face her. He wound his long front legs around her neck and buried his face in her warm woolly chest.

"My darling, I too will never leave you. Not 'ere." He patted his heart. "You and me, we are somewhere always in ze dance, no? In Time. Out of Time. For all Time."

Jake padded gently up to the two of them. "It's time, Rico. Myrtle's love will protect her. And maybe one day that love will draw us together again. Who knows?" He swallowed hard. "Sergeant Pepper, Darius, are you ready?"

Slowly, Maverico loosened his grip and stepped away from Myrtle and the spyders began cutting loose all the various threads that had been used to lead The General there. Only one remained, which they knotted loosely around Myrtle's horn.

"You've got to be able to get free once, well, you know, once the trouble starts," said Sergeant Pepper. "That horn's sharp enough to cut these threads anyway."

The cats and the badgers surrounded The General and began nudging him forward. His low growling turned to curses and then to a terrified scream as he moved closer and closer to the mouth of the tunnel. Myrtle went directly behind him, butting him with her horn till he was inside. Quick as a flash she followed, filling the space so he could not escape. She turned to look back at her friends one last time and then the tunnel itself began to turn, slowly at first and then faster and faster. Myrtle and The General turned too.

"Quick Myrtle, cut the thread," yelled Beatrice. But by then the tunnel was turning so fast that Beatrice could not tell whether Myrtle had managed to free herself of her wretched charge. And then the two animals disappeared from view.

Jake and Beatrice and Maverico turned to each other. Between them was an enormous emptiness – a Myrtle-shaped hole that was so much bigger than Myrtle herself had even been.

Beatrice thought of Myrtle shivering and scavenging in the Ice Age once more, without her grand passion to keep her warm. And then she thought about The General. Where would he end up? Would the tunnel claim all of his skeleton this time and not just a leg? How could she have done that to him? To anyone? Would it not, after all, have been kinder to kill him as Belladonna had wished? Perhaps she, Beatrice, was in truth the cruel, vengeful one?

"Did we do the right thing?" Her voice was weak and shaky.

From his bed of bracken Rufus looked up at them with rheumy eyes. "We call ourselves the Muscateers, but Myrtle, she was the true warrior, all along. Such courage. Such love. History will record her great sacrifice, my Princess. But I fear it was indeed the only way."

"I agree, Bee." Jake sighed. "An' as for The General, I can tell you're worried about him too. But he chose his fate the first time he went down there, when he was after gaining Leon's kingdom for all Time. The wrong thing was that he came back out again at all. He's just back where he belongs, I guess. And, hopefully, everything else will be soon enough. Oh-oh here it comes. Hold on to your fur, folks."

A great wind tore through the trees. A strange wind. Not the sort that goes forwards and backwards, or tosses things up and drops them down again. This was a circular wind that started at the Time Tunnel and went all around the Wildwoods, sucking into itself air and water and trees and animals. The mystery was that the four muscateers and Grubsta and the badgers and Freddy and George and the starlings and the rooks and the spydinis remained absolutely still while the whirlwind raged around them. Not a fur nor a feather nor a spyder thread was disturbed. In fact their very breath seemed suspended. Yet around them the tornado circled wildly. Beatrice watched as mini-Cedrics slithered from all directions as though drawn by a magnet. A hundred red-eyed, black-marked snakes came together and joined to form one magnificent sea-serpent. Cedric's eyes glittered as he sought out Jake, standing frozen to the spot. Slowly the sea-serpent raised himself from the ground and bowed again, low. The red eye winked and Cedric slithered into the tunnel and out of sight.

The circling air grew thick and opaque until soon Beatrice could see nothing at all. But the wind filled her ears with its moans and groans. Then she was glad to be blind because she understood what was happening. These were the cries of the Nameless returning to whence they had come. She felt the force of the suction coming from the Time Tunnel, even though it did not affect her in the slightest. She smelt the black, whirling element around her, sulphur and sickness, hatred and hurt, death and decay. For a split second Belladonna moved within her again. *No, Bella,* Beatrice told her silently, *I need you to stay.* She felt Belladonna settle, like a deep sigh, and she knew what it meant. Peace, at last.

Around her, the air slowly cleared. Against a pale pink sky, the dark arms of the trees reached up to the new sun. And there were Jake and Rufus and Maverico awakening, as if from a dream. Beside them sat Grubsta and the badgers. The ground was covered with silvery spyder threads. Green grass and dead bracken covered the area where the tunnel had been. Above her the bats began to form squadrons again, but not for warfare. They flitted off in formation into the woods searching for cool clefts of rock where they could continue their hibernation.

The war was over. For a few minutes the woods were completely still, the sort of stillness that follows movement as silence follows song. The General was gone and the Nameless with him. The squirrels and all the creatures who had been taken over by the Nameless were free once more. She heard George give one long, soft hoot. And then, all over the Wildwoods, the birds began to sing.

CHAPTER 34
ALL FOUR ONE

"Thank heavens for a bit of peace and quiet!"

There was no mistaking that voice. Beatrice looked up, fear clawing at her belly. High on a ledge in the rock face, white and glowing and perfect, sat the great Sheba herself.

"Really Beatrice, you have surpassed yourself this time. As if it is not enough to change your own room into something resembling a laundry, you have to turn the whole wood upside down and inside out as well. Why is it that everywhere you go you bring chaos? Thank goodness I was here to sort it out."

Beatrice gasped in disbelief. After all, she was the one who had travelled through time and infiltrated The General's cave to rescue Sheba's beloved Candy. It was Beatrice, not Sheba, who had fought The General and his followers, who had battled the Nameless and restored the Wildwoods. Where had Sheba been then, and what had she done – other than spruce up poor little Grubsta to within an inch of his life?

These words, and others, sprang to her lips, but they got no further. For the first time since she had left the attic Beatrice felt like a helpless, fearful kitten. She searched inside her belly for Belladonna. Surely Bella would know how to deal with Sheba? But even Belladonna was silent before Sheba's taut, furious presence.

Beatrice looked over at Jake and Maverico. But Jake was sitting calmly with his tail tucked around him as though

267

nothing had happened at all. As though a hole in time had not opened up and closed again. As though there was no such thing as the Nameless. As though he had not just led an army of badgers to victory in a pitched battle. As for Maverico, he had stopped his snivelling over the loss of Myrtle and was lying on his back, his long limbs and tail stretched out, almost like a corpse. Rufus, meanwhile, had managed to raise himself from the ground and was trying desperately to stand to attention and bow to the Queen, though Beatrice could see his legs trembling. Grubsta was doing his best to hide behind him.

She looked into the trees. Jack Daw and the starlings and the rooks had all disappeared. The only sign that anything had happened at all were the spyder webs threaded through every tree and rock and blade of grass. King Billy and the badgers were nowhere to be seen. They must have dived down the many entrances leading to Badger City. So much for their valour, thought Beatrice, contemptuously. It seemed that facing up to the Nameless was one thing but facing up to Queen Sheba quite another – though Beatrice had to admit that if she herself had actually been able to move, she might have followed them. As it was she remained paralysed, impaled on the spear of her mother's fury. Could this be the same Sheba whose wailing had filled the woods when Beatrice had been captured by George and the Nameless? She remembered what Candy had said about Sheba being especially hard on Beatrice because of her special powers. But already Beatrice felt those powers shrinking away to nothing.

It was Rufus who finally spoke. His voice was weak and wavering, but he carried himself fiercely upright. Beatrice could see the effort it was costing him.

"Please, Your Majesty, don't shout at her. Beatrice has shown courage and ingenuity beyond her years. More than that, I can assure you that her powers are developing nicely.

Why, without her I would probably be…well I wouldn't be here at all."

"Without her none of us would be here," snapped Sheba. "Heading off into the woods without a by-your-leave. Throwing yourselves down the Time Tunnel as if it were a helter-skelter at some public amusement park. Dragging a pre-historic carthorse into this century with no regard for the laws of physics."

"Ees not a cart 'orse. Ees a woolly rhino. Very rare. And no one dragged 'er. She came for love." Maverico had roused himself and was on his feet again.

"Aah, it moves!" Sheba gave a tinkling laugh, like ice cubes falling into cut glass. "For a moment I thought it was an exhibit from The General's cave. Oh yes," she looked at Beatrice, "you thought you were the only one, didn't you? But The General and I, we go back a long way – to ancient Egypt even. He wanted me to move in, you know to that foul cave of his. Can you imagine? But I made him give me this little place up here. It has the advantage that he can't possibly reach me, with that leg of his. And anyway this place is, well, let's just say it's more what I'm used to. You can come up if you like, as long as you wipe your paws."

The four muscateers sat, rooted to the spot by fear.

"You misunderstand me. That is not a request. It is a command."

"B…but what about Rufus?" stammered Beatrice. "He won't manage the climb."

"Oh, I'm sure you can persuade those spyders of yours to help out. That's if they dare show their faces. There's plenty of silk left over from The General's harness. You need to do something with all that thread anyway. It's making the place look untidy."

"You go ahead, the rest of you," Rufus panted. "I'll be along in a minute."

Beatrice looked across at Jake for help. But Jake still did not move. And even more worryingly, he did not speak or laugh. He seemed smaller somehow, diminished, as though he were disappearing before her very eyes.

"Go on Jake, Rico," she heard Rufus whisper. "It's time. Not just for me but for all of us. You too, Grub."

Jake looked across at Beatrice and his eyes were so sad she thought her heart would break looking into them.

"Time for what?" she asked. "Jake, what's wrong? Tell me… Rico?"

But Maverico had already started climbing the cliff face. His movements were sluggish and awkward, like a puppet whose strings were too loose. Jake began to get up too, but slowly, as if in a dream.

"Nothing's wrong, Sweet Bee. Everything is just as it should be. Guess that's the problem. Best get going now. Time for one last adventure eh?"

"What do you mean, last adventure?"

But Jake had already set off and so Beatrice followed, her heart leaden with foreboding. They climbed the steep rocks together. Jake was not his usual confident self and twice nearly missed his footing but Belladonna seemed to have got her voice back and shouted instructions in Beatrice's ear, so between them they managed, while Grubsta stumbled behind. Sergeant Pepper and Darius had both turned up to lead the work on Rufus's harness and they were so quick that Rufus arrived at the entrance to Sheba's cave at the same time as Beatrice and Jake.

"Well, don't hang about outside. Come in." Sheba's mood appeared to have softened. "It's not exactly an Egyptian palace, but it will do for now."

"After you, Princess," Jake bowed low and for once Beatrice was not sure whether he was joking or not.

She put her front paws across the threshold and instantly the cave filled with light. It did not have the quality of ordinary daylight and it was not like the electric light in the attic either. This came from somewhere inside, like the light from the sun. And it revealed an interior that was beautiful beyond imagination.

Sheba's cave was a true palace, made out of the finest crystal. The rear was lined with rose quartz and amethyst and the floor shimmered with the deep blue of lapis lazuli. Wide bands of lilac and emerald reached from the ceiling to the ground. Elsewhere russet and brown veins threaded daintily through white quartz. On one side the wall folded over and billowed out like a curtain in a breeze, encrusted with diamonds. Stools and tables rose from the floor in sparkling golds and yellows. The ceiling was criss-crossed by beams of banded green agate and hung with chandeliers of rubies and sapphires, ambers and jades. For one fleeting moment, Beatrice thought of the dead crow at the heart of The General's cave, but it was impossible to hold on to images of ugliness in a place as beautiful as this.

Amethyst, aquamarine, cobalt, citrine. The words spun round and round in Beatrice's head. Words Sheba had taught her in those long hours of lessons and reminiscences. Beatrice had dismissed them all as fantasy, but here they were, for real, in the middle of the Wildwoods and just a stone's throw from The General's disgusting hideout.

"Do close your mouth dear. It's very unbecoming to be gawping like a commoner. You, of all people, should understand this sort of place."

Beatrice closed her mouth obediently, too amazed by her surroundings to ask what her mother meant by that remark. But then she turned to look at Sheba and her jaw dropped open once more. The old Queen sat quite still in the middle of the crystal cave but something was happening to her creamy white fur. It was reflecting all the colours from the walls and the ceiling and the floor. One moment she was a pale translucent green, the next she was pink, then lilac then mauve, then silvery white. Sheba had turned herself into a living jewel, like an opal or a moonstone.

"You really do have a crystal palace, Mummy. But why didn't you show me this before?"

"Well, darling, you didn't seem interested for one thing." Sheba flicked her tail dismissively and it flashed in shades of purple and turquoise. "You were happy enough with that tacky box of Christmas decorations. I'm hoping you have developed more powers of discrimination by now. Candy, darling, just one more minute and then you can take a break."

For the first time, Beatrice spied Candy at the very back of the cave. She was standing next to Gangsta, who was still bound by the spyder threads. He lay on his back with his front paws tied behind his head and his back legs stretched out and knotted together at the other end. Candy was enthusiastically washing his exposed belly. With each lick of her rough little tongue Gangsta winced as though he had been whipped. She stepped back to admire her work.

"Hey Beatrice, what do you think? A bit better, I'd say." Candy looked pleased with herself. Gangsta gave a slow, strangled moan.

"Very nice, Candy," said Beatrice noting, with a flash of jealousy, that Candy's white fur also shimmered with crystal colours. Her own markings, freed from the spydernet, had turned themselves into a desert scene. Black pyramids stood on golden sands against a bleached white sky.

"Well, Candy dear, it's a start." Sheba's tone was mildly approving. "We'll turn him over in a minute and perhaps the boys here can have a go too. There are so many layers to drill down. It took me days to do that dumb fellow over there."

Grubsta had a weird expression on his face, as though he did not know whether to be angry at being called a dumb fellow or proud of his new cleanliness. Gangsta just looked terrified at the thought of Jake and Maverico setting to work on him.

"So come on now, Queenie," Jake's voice had something of the old insolence about it. "Tell us how you found this place and why you've been hiding it so long."

Sheba cast a cold eye on Jake and Beatrice felt the familiar shiver go through her. But she was relieved to see that at least her friend seemed to be more like his usual self now. He gave a long stretch and rolled over on his side to listen.

"This place, as you call it, is many thousands of years old. It was my palace in Egypt when I lived there. Or at least one room of my palace. That was before I got caught up by The General and he dragged me through that wretched Time Tunnel to these god-forsaken woods. I managed to escape, of course, and that was where dear Leon found me. I told him a bit of a fib at the time about where I had come from, but he worked it out himself in the end." She sniffed daintily.

"I could not go back of course. It would have been far too dangerous. It is still a miracle that I survived the journey so… purrfectly." Sheba cast an appreciative glance at herself. "But dear Leon did it for me. He said he would build my palace right here and he went through that wretched Time Tunnel over and over, back to ancient Egypt, bringing bits of crystal back with him, one by one. We built it together secretly. Well, I supervised and he did it, with help from the magpies, though I had to get very firm with them about their thieving habits, I'm afraid."

At the mention of King Leon's name Jake and Rico stood sharply to attention and even Rufus stumbled to his feet again. "So Leon is here then – my father is here?" asked Beatrice, excitedly.

For the first time in Beatrice's life, she saw her mother look embarrassed, even ashamed.

"Sadly, no. He had to make many trips to create this beauty that you see around you. And each time he returned it was

273

as though he had left a little of his strength behind him. Gradually he got thinner and weaker so that he was almost transparent. And then one day he went off as usual and… well, he never came back again." Sheba looked far into the distance, somewhere beyond the cave and the Wildwoods. A single tear dropped onto the lapis floor. Beatrice watched it solidify into clear crystal. She remembered her mother's wails when she had been captured by George.

"Mummy," she said, her voice trembling a little. "I heard you, you know. In the woods. When the Nameless got me. You were crying then."

Sheba's eyes became narrow slits – like the ones medieval archers use to fire their arrows through. Beatrice flinched automatically, in anticipation.

"Don't be ridiculous Beatrice. What you heard was a very special war cry. It was to summon help after you had allowed all those ghouls and ruffians to ride rough shod over my Queendom. Who do you think summoned that cart horse there out of the Ice Age? And those awful snakes? Not those great clowns over there, that's for sure," she indicated Jake, Maverico and Rufus, "though they might think that's what happened. It requires very special powers to travel through time and to enable others to do so."

"But we did it and we were safe. Jake says you can do it safely if you travel for love," said Beatrice hopefully. She tried to remember what Candy had told her about Sheba only being strict because Beatrice was special. Surely that meant her mother must love her a little bit.

"Love!" Sheba laughed scornfully. "A primitive carthorse and a slithering reptile? What do they know of love? No, they were simply obeying orders, mark my words. My orders. With dear Leon, of course, it was different."

"Oh, Mummy," Beatrice interrupted, excitement over-riding the pain of her mother's cold response, "we've seen him!" But Jake kicked her hard on the rump and she stopped abruptly.

"I don't think so dear. You must have been dreaming. I think he's gone now. Forever. All those journeys through time, they were just too much for him."

"I guess it's a bit like The General. He only had to give 'em his leg – and his honour, or what was left of it. Old Leon, he gave his strength. These here bodies, they're just not meant for time travel." Jake yawned. "One trip and I'm jiggered."

"Ees right. And love, across Time, this ees very 'ard," said Maverico who was thinking of Myrtle. "Eet also takes its toll."

Rufus said nothing. He was struggling to breathe.

"Rufus?" Beatrice stood over him anxiously. She felt her markings beginning to move again. They were sliding towards the floor, where Rufus lay, his glorious green eyes now pale and clouded. She did not try to stop them. Rufus was shivering. Perhaps they would keep him warm.

"Oh, my Princess," he gasped. "I wish I could serve you longer. It has been my greatest joy, since the moment you created me."

"Oh no, Rufus, I never created you. Why, if I could do that I would make you better and it seems…" her voice faltered. She looked over at Jake and Maverico. "I think he's delirious."

"I wish he was, my sweet, sweet Bee. I thought you'd have realised by now." Jake looked away from her and a tear dropped from his eyes too. Beatrice watched it turn into a ball of solid black jet and roll away.

"Rico," she cried, turning desperately towards him "what's going on?"

"My Bella Beatrizia. My Bella Donna. My Beauty. My Self. Is you who named me Maverico – a name magnifico. I 'ope I 'ave lived up to it." His tears dripped onto the floor. Beatrice watched them crystallise. Black tourmaline and white selenite, known as Angel's Wing.

"Me too," said Gangsta, still bound by his spyder threads. Grubsta just looked at her silently and nodded his head.

"But that's ridiculous. Why I can see you in front of me now. This is your fault." Beatrice turned on Sheba. "You told me they were imaginary friends and now they believe you. You're a cruel liar. You sit here in your crystal cave doing nothing but admiring yourself, while we are out there saving the Wildwoods from destruction. Ask King Billy. Or George. Or Jack Daw. They'll tell you. Even the squirrels will have to admit it now."

"Really, Beatrice, if you are going to speak like that I think it's time you went back to the attic." Sheba looked across at Jake. "I thought she would have had the intelligence to work it out for herself. Or you would have explained it to her."

"Explained what Jake?" Beatrice was getting beyond anger. She was beginning to feel frightened. Jake's cuddly form seemed thinner, frailer, almost translucent. She remembered what Sheba had said about Leon fading away from too many trips down the Time Tunnel.

Jake sighed. "Well, Bee, you know how you sort of summoned up Belladonna when you needed a bit of help from the dark side?"

"Of course I do, but I think actually she was there all along. I just didn't know her. And anyway, she is inside me. But you and Rico and Roof, you're outside of me. And you're my friends. We're the four muscateers." She thought of all the times they had looked after her – danced with her, fought for her, comforted her.

"Exactly Bee." Jake looked weary and his voice was getting quieter. "What do we always say? *One Four All and All Four One*. It's not exactly like you made us up. But you was just pretty sad and desperate and you'll remember you didn't have right good control of your markings back then. And well, you just sort of went to pieces. And we was the pieces. And pretty soon now you'll pull yourself together and I guess that will be the end of us. You gotta be yourself now. Your whole self. So no hard feelings or anything. It's been a grand run."

"That's ridiculous. I mean, if you three are just me in pieces, or pieces of me, then what are Gangsta over there and Grubsta and The General? And Candy for that matter?"

Jake considered. "This is mighty difficult to explain, sweet Bee, especially when I'm so jiggered, but, well we all have our dark side. So Gangsta's sort of my Belladonna and Grubsta's Rico's and The General, he's Rufus's. That's why he wouldn't rightly have killed Roof, it would have been like suicide. But when The General went down that tunnel again, well, that just about did for old Roof. He's sort of split through Time now. So I guess things can't go on."

"So you're just a story I've made up and now it's over?"

"You never made us up Bee. We was already there some-where – like you said with Belladonna. We was just waiting for you to look at us, so's we could get started, I guess."

"Now you're beginning to sound like Mr Schrödinger," said Beatrice. "And anyway you haven't explained about Candy. Or Sheba. Please don't tell me I made *her* up."

"Ah, now Sheba is a bit different. Wouldn't you know?"

Sheba preened herself at these words. Her eyes misted over and she began to chant. But her voice was faint and hollow. As though it came not from herself but from somewhere very far away.

> *Ishtar and Aphrodite*
> *Ubasti and Sekhmet*
> *Queen of the Night*
> *The Great Mother*
> *The Great Warrior*
> *The Great Cat*

Sheba's voice faded away. She sat quite still, her eyes unblinking, frozen like a statue. But the caves still echoed with the strange names. The sound tingled up and down Beatrice's spine. She looked at Jake.

"I suppose you're going to tell me what that's about too?"

Jake paused for a moment.

"Well, it's difficult to explain, Bee. Words don't rightly speak the full meaning. But Sheba's like *The* Cat. The One. Where it all began."

"You mean in Egypt?"

"Maybe. Maybe before that even. She's like the *idea* of a Cat. What you might call the archetype. Holds the form through the centuries. Maybe even the universe if there's cats in them other galaxies up there." He flicked his tail to indicate the sky outside the cave.

"I don't understand," she said. "You said she was an old fraud."

Jake smiled.

"Well, that might be true too. But that's just the personality she's come with. Gotta live in this world and this time and this story. 'Nother time she might be a sweet-natured old lady cat or a warrior. Don't mean that's her soul. You see, the important thing is Sheba carries all the cat memories there've ever been in that great white fur coat of hers. An' the little black bits. All there ever was and all there ever will be too, I'm guessing. Jus' like we was all a part of you – only bigger. An' every now an' then she actually takes physical form on Earth. When she's needed. Don't mean we've got to like her!"

"But if Sheba's the One, whatever that is," Beatrice's tone was derisory, "then how do you account for Candy? She looks just like a mini-Sheba. Which makes two in my book, not one."

"Well, Candy now, far as I know she's Sheba's Belladonna. 'Cept with old Sheba this time it was the other way around and she's the cute side. Sheba wanted someone to keep you occupied when she wasn't around. Someone who loved you and wouldn't lead you astray. Didn't quite work out how she'd planned, I guess. But I tell you one thing Bee, it's been the best adventure ever."

"How can it be an adventure if it's not real. If you're not real." Beatrice could feel the tears welling in her own eyes now. "If you're just me, then you're not even my friends. None of you. And I'm all alone. There's no one but me. And all these adventures with Dino and Cedric and Myrtle and the Nameless, I suppose they're not real then either.

"You're not my lovely Jake. And you Rico, you're not magnificent at all. You're just some crazy part of me that fancies himself as a Latin dancer who's in love with a make-believe mammoth.

"And Rufus. You're not noble and dashing – you are just a pathetic piece of ginger fur that dropped off my belly one day."

She turned back to Jake, but he looked at her with such love that for a moment she forgot what she was going to say.

"I thought you were my special friend in all the world. You made me feel safe and loved. But you're nobody. Nothing at all. How stupid was I?"

"No more stupid than me, I guess." Jake was panting his words out now and there was something strange happening with his eyes, like a light going on and off, getting fainter each time. "You were my special friend too. There's no one like you, Baybee. Not in the whole world. Thing is, you'll always be Bee, but I won't always be Jake. I could be anyone you want or need. I s'pose I could even be someone you don't even think you need at all, sometimes. Or don't even like. If that's what you need.

"You and me, Bee, we were good. So good. But when it comes down to it I'm just like a thought in your head. Just passing through…." His voice faded away.

"I'm not going to think about any of you at all," Beatrice began. But then she stopped because something very strange was happening to Sheba. A pillar of light streamed from the top of the cave to the bottom, right where the Queen stood. Beatrice had not noticed any opening in the roof. Yet the light had to come from somewhere. It shimmered and danced so brightly that Beatrice could hardly make out the shape of her mother inside it. She felt her eyes brimming with tears. That must be it. They were affecting her vision. It was just an optical illusion. Another illusion.

Quickly she turned her back so her treacherous friends would not see her tears. But they spilled out, littering the cave floor with crystal – quartz, amber, obsidian, tiger's eye.

There was only one thing to do. She stepped towards the cave entrance and gathered herself to address them for the last time.

"Mr Schrödinger was wrong. You weren't dead *or* alive, because you didn't even exist. You're all fakes, not real friends at all. I won't have anything to do with you. If I'm on my own, then that's what I'll be."

She heard Rufus's gasping breath. "Farewell, my Princess."

Then Maverico's quavering tones. "It has been…magnifico."

And finally Jake. "Sweet times, sweet Bee. Keep warm."

She heard a strange, ghostly laugh, like glass shattering. Sheba's laugh. And then she felt a sharp pain in her chest – as though a sliver of sharp crystal had cut into her heart.

From what seemed like very far away three voices began to chant.

"All Four One and One Four All."

Despite herself, Beatrice turned to join in their song one last time. But when she looked back the cave was quite empty. There was only the echo of voices chanting, becoming more and more distant. And then silence.

In the middle of the cave, where the glorious Sheba had stood, a single stalagmite rose from the puddled floor. But there was no pillar of light, no gold, no lapis lazuli, no amethyst, no jade. No Candy, no Gangsta or Grubsta. And no muscateers. Only grey rocks, dripping onto dank stone. She shivered, reaching for Belladonna deep inside. But even Belladonna had gone. She was completely alone.

And then, as she gazed, something stirred inside the cave. It was large and shapeless and moved like the wind so she could not see it properly. When she looked directly at it, it disappeared. But, out of the corner of her eye, she saw it float from the mouth of the cave and come towards her. It wrapped itself round her like a gentle breeze and then it disappeared and all she felt was a wave of warmth and tenderness. Suddenly her fur seemed thicker and more lustrous. She could sense her markings moving, but now they felt different – as though they were snuggling into her, taking root, not struggling to escape. She looked down, expecting to find ugly splodges or ridiculous round stripes, but her paws and chest and belly were immaculately white and she could see some very elegant, perfectly symmetrical patches of gold on her flanks. Her tail was delicately ringed in black and gold and thick black fur encircled her shoulders. The gentle wind whispered in her ear. *All Four One.*

She took a step and was surprised to find her legs insisted on going sideways instead of forwards. They seemed to be dancing the Paso Doblé, like Maverico. The next moment her hips started to wiggle as well. That made her laugh, despite herself. The trouble was she had no idea how to stop them.

But then a sudden impulse made her stand to attention and take a bow, just as Rufus used to do. Except now there was no one else there so she had to bow to herself, which felt a bit strange. The sort of thing Sheba would approve of probably. Still, at least it stopped the dancing. She was just wondering how she would get anywhere if this sort of thing carried on when she heard a voice. She looked around but nobody was there. Actually, now she came to think about it, the sound seemed to come from inside her head, not outside at all. But there it was, clear as a bell. The same dear beloved voice she knew so well.

"Told you we wasn't going nowhere. Bee-Loved Sweet Bee."

A mischievous chuckle rang around her head making her feel quite dizzy. It spread through her arms and legs, along her torso and tail, and settled deep in her heart, right next to the sliver of shattered crystal from Sheba's chilly laugh.

Above her, the sky was clear blue. The midday sun blazed with fire and the hills were a soft green, melting to purple at the horizon. She thought of the story Jake had told her about her birth and all the colours she had been born with and how Leon had hidden them for safekeeping. Were they real? When would she get them back? Would she have to find them herself or would someone bring them to her? There was no harm in looking, after all.

Beatrice sniffed the winter air and smiled to hear the squirrels still squabbling in the trees. A jackdaw flew overhead and landed on a branch just a few feet away. It looked at her quizzically, but said nothing. The trees were swagged with fine webs, glistening in the sunshine. A spyder scuttled up a tree trunk.

Beatrice stepped right out of the cave – without dancing this time – and made her way carefully down the steep face. Everything looked familiar and yet completely different. She took a step forward and as she did so a strange new path opened up in front of her. It was cobbled and shiny and inviting. She stretched out another paw and noticed as she did so that the path ahead grew longer. This was fun. Somewhere in the empty sky a bird was singing. Streams of water tumbled from the high hills all around. In the distance she caught a glimpse of a fine stag, his white antlers catching the winter sun. The beautiful, wild world was all before her. It was, as

Jake would have said, a world of endless possibilities. Her markings shivered with excitement.

She drew them close and took another step.

ACKNOWLEDGEMENTS

This book has been a long time coming, so thank you to all those who have supported, encouraged and, when necessary, badgered me to keep going when I was losing heart.

Special thanks to Jean Davison and Graeme Hall who listened patiently and commented thoughtfully on chapter after chapter in the early stages. Without you I am sure the book would never have been completed.

Also to Jane Macaskie, Helen Scott, Katie Tribe and Meic Goodyear for reading early drafts and for their support and constructive criticism along the way, to Sophie Ellis for her beautiful cover design and to Rafael at Formatting Experts for his expertise, attention to detail and patience in explaining technicalities to my non-technical mind.

Most of all, I have to thank the woodland creatures and my own little corner of the Wildwoods for providing me with daily inspiration – the birds, badgers, bats, beetles, butterflies, spiders, foxes, squirrels and cats, with whom I have been privileged to share this magical space.

ABOUT THE AUTHOR

Annie Goodyear is a former journalist and award-winning TV producer. She now lives in woodlands in Yorkshire where she spends a lot of time watching the birds, the wildlife and the cat community when she should actually be writing. That is one of the reasons why she took so long to write this book.

She occasionally blogs about the real Wildwoods at
www.mywildwoods.com

Printed in Great Britain
by Amazon

38509495R00177